1975

ook may be kept

# FOURTEEN DAYS

# There's Gold in Your Golden Age

Other books by the same author:

*Doorways to Prospects*

*Door Openers on Parade*

*How to Conquer Fears, Worries and Frustrations in 30 Hours*

# There's Gold in Your Golden Age

A guide and a challenge to you who wish to grow with your older age and make your coming years the best yet to be. . . .

*By*

MAXWELL S. CAGAN

*Publishers*

T. S. DENISON & COMPANY, INC.

Minneapolis

Dedicated to my wife,

BETTY,

who gave up many weekends and
leisure hours to make this book possible.

# Contents

# Introduction

You are the most important person alive today, because insofar as you are concerned no one else matters so much and no one else can be so deeply interested in your well-being, in what you are, in what you do and in what you make of your good years yet to come as you, yourself.

Of course, as a married person your spouse may love you dearly, as a parent your family and your children may be very close to you, and as a neighbor your friends may be ready to do everything possible to make life easier and happier for you. But all of that has little value or meaning unless and until you "get into the act" and help yourself first.

Perhaps you are one of the fortunate few who has no problems and needs no help. You may be in excellent health, be well fixed financially and fully adjusted to your age, your status and your surroundings. If this is your position, all the more power and credit to you.

But, if you have fears, needs and problems; if life is not so sweet and bright for you, and if you want to do something about it this book may be helpful to you. Then it may become as personal as if meant and written only for you, because it takes up many of the needs and problems you face day by day. It provides directives and suggests specific ways of how to help yourself and how to help others, if you so desire, to attain a greater measure of joy and happiness in the golden years still before you.

Most of your problems as a senior adult stem from the fact that you live longer. The social order you face today, the economic factors involved, the civic and welfare agencies, the members of your family, the community, the public officials and the nation as a whole have not as yet accepted your longevity as an established fact. Hence, no provisions have been made to keep in step with your longer life expectancy and with all that such longevity entails in needs, in care, in services, in facilities and in mental attitudes.

Nearly ten per cent of our total population is near or past sixty-five years of age and the number is growing at the rate of better than five hundred thousand a year. Many of them have no way to deal with their economic, physical, social and psychical problems. Most of them are thrown upon their own meager resources and in the face of ever-mounting costs of living and medical care life grows more and more difficult for them.

Some of them have social security benefits or old-age assistance grants, retirement pensions or private incomes. But in the majority of cases, such income is not big enough to provide the right food, the needed medical care, the proper housing facilities, the leisure time activities and all the other requisites for decent, adequate and dignified living.

This book is intended to be a guide and a challenge to you who want to grow with your older age and make the most of every passing day. It is also intended to show you how to help others, how to become the leader of a group, how to join forces with other senior adult clubs, how to foster national awareness of your needs and how to engender full public acceptance of your rightful place in your community.

With those objectives in view, the following topics will be covered: 1. Your Preparation for Retirement. 2. You and Your Older Age. 3. Your Physical Well-being. 4. Your Mental Status. 5. Your Economic Maintenance. 6. Your Housing Accommodations. 7. Your Leisure Time Activities. 8. Your

Social Relationships. 9. Your Place in the Sun. 10. Your Guide to Better Speeches and to Group Formations.

Some of these topics will be covered in detail and others touched upon only briefly. It will be up to you to follow those of particular interest to you. But whatever your interest might be, let the pages that follow be your guide. Let them encourage you to learn, to know, to appreciate. Let them inspire you to do things for yourself and at the same time help others.

You will find many individuals, organizations and governmental agencies ready to help you. Among them are the U. S. Printing Office in Washington, D. C., the adult schools in your city, the social and welfare agencies, the service clubs, the YMCA and the YWCA, the church affiliations, Community Centers, the Gerontological Society, the Senior Citizen Service Centers and your state and county Committees on Aging.

Let this book also be a challenge to you. Let it intensify your desire to do more about your unmet needs and problems. Let it inspire you to join hands with others in your age group, so as to work together and make your voice heard over the land. Then, as surely as you are reading these lines, you will add beauty, meaning and importance to everyday living. Then you will surely take your rightful place in your community and find the gold in your golden age.

MAXWELL S. CAGAN

Los Angeles, California

# CHAPTER ONE

# How to Prepare Yourself
# for Retirement

If you are past 65 years of age, have no financial problems, are well adjusted to your status and surroundings and fully enjoy your leisure days, you could render a priceless service to those who have not prepared themselves for their retirement years.

The need to "plan early for later living" is growing more and more important since the number of those reaching 65 is increasing at the rate of nearly 500,000 each year. We will have close to 20 million Americans, 65 years and over, within the next few years, and many of them could remain physically and mentally fit, as well as useful and self-supporting, if they were to be properly trained and adequately prepared for later retirement.

The important thing to do by those who still have time before reaching their official retirement age is not to wait until the last few months but to start working, planning and training *now*, whether it be five, ten or more years ahead of time. It is the steps one takes *now*, it is the plans one makes *now*, that will determine to a large extent the kind of retirement one will have, later.

Too many people have false illusions about their retirement days. Ask the average person past fifty about his plans for his leisure days to come and he will chuckle and say: "Don't be silly. I don't have to prepare myself to loaf and take things easy. It will come naturally . . ." Or, "I'll be too busy doing the things I wanted to do to worry about the time available . . ." Or, "I'll throw my alarm clock away and luxuriate in bed till noon . . ." Or, "I'll catch up on my reading . . . I'll watch my favorite TV programs . . . I'll go to night clubs . . . I'll go fishing, hunting, swimming, camping, prospecting . . ."

Unfortunately, none of those illusions comes to pass. They fade away too soon and leave only misery in their place. Staying in bed till noon, watching TV programs, hunting or swimming, reading, dancing, fishing, and other similar activities can be a fair share of one's leisure time programs, but they in themselves cannot possibly round out hour after hour and day after day of time and "nothing planned to do . . ."

Idle hands and an idle mind, coupled with the lack of prearranged workable and satisfying plans can become an unbearable burden and do great harm, physically, mentally and emotionally. You need but look around you and notice those older people you meet, who appear to be lost, bewildered, miserable, who because of it quickly succumb to debilitating illnesses, to realize how important it is to plan and to prepare one's self for enjoyable retirement.

Those plans should embody gradual changes in occupational and recreational activities as well as mental attitudes. They should include a realistic evaluation of your older age and what it implies, an appraisal of your leanings and interests, a careful analysis of future income and expenses with due regard to your probable medical needs, a thorough check of future living accommodations especially if you plan to move to some other city or state, a consideration of your future contacts with children or members of your family, an awareness of sense impairments and infirmities and the readiness to live with such disabilities.

The twenty steps to consider as given in the following pages are not complete and all-inclusive. The sequences are purely accidental and are not to be taken as an indication of importance. Your needs or the situation of those with whom you expect to work may differ and what is of little value to you may be all-important to someone else.

Among the things to be considered, in preparing yourself or in helping others to prepare themselves for retirement, are:

## 1. LIVING ACCOMMODATIONS

The fact that if there are children they will no longer be at home. They will have homes and families of their own. They may be scattered in different cities or states and even be outside of the United States. Thus, as a parent, you may have to reconcile yourself to live where you are or where you intend to go, without having your children with you or near you.

On the other hand, because you will no longer be tied down to a job, you may prefer to live close to or with your children. This may pose special problems which only you and your children can solve. For instance, if you have more than one child and each lives at a different place you will have to weigh carefully all the pros and cons before you decide to follow one or live with another.

Among the factors you will have to take into account will be the question of compatibility. How well do you get along with a given son-in-law or daughter-in-law? How do their children take to you? How much room do they have for themselves? Can they accommodate you without inconvenience to themselves and to you? What is their status in the community? How will you fit into their routines of living? Will your presence be a help or a detriment to them? How much or how little can you contribute to your support? What is your general health? Do you require special diets or care? These and other similar questions need to be asked and properly answered before you dispose of your own living quarters and come to live with a child.

And, if there is more than one parent, there is even greater need for careful evaluation of all the factors involved. When most families lived in rural areas the addition of one or more persons to live in the same house was not a problem. There was room to spare. This is not true in urban living. Your married son or daughter has no extra rooms, and your living with him or with her, even under ideal personal relationships, may be difficult for all.

If you have more than one child in town and each one of them wants you, there is another problem. Would it be more advisable for you to retain your own living quarters and your independence or dispose of your property and go to one of your children? If so, who shall be the one? Who shall have the pleasure or the burden? And which section of the city, assuming you live in a cosmopolitan center, is best suited to your needs?

If you decide to keep your home and share it with one of your children, you face another problem. Who shall be the one and how will such a move on your part react on the feelings of the rest? It is easy enough to say to a child: "Come, live with me. We'll get along . . ." Feeling and sentiment are for it, but in the face of stern reality, the sharing of quarters with a married child, especially where grandchildren may be involved, is not always the best thing for all concerned. There are bound to be heartaches and resentments. It is in the nature of things. . . .

Of course, there are many instances where parents and married children live together and are happy together. But those cases are the exception. Circumstances change and feelings change. There are bound to be differences of opinion. There are sure to be clashes and hard feelings from time to time, especially if there is a touch of bitterness, a trace of resentment, or a modicum of regret on either side.

It was never meant for two and three generations to live together in close quarters. There are differences in views and opinions, in likes and preferences, in habits and behavior, in beliefs and attitudes that show up quickly. These have a way of magnifying and multiplying themselves as the parent takes or does not take sides in some family misunderstanding.

If your retirement age is already upon you and your finances do not permit you to live apart and independently from your children, you may be forced to swallow your pride and go to live with a child, with all the tribulations such enforced sharing of living quarters entails. But if you still have a few years before you reach your retirement, do everything in your power to have enough in cash or in assets later on, so that you could retain your home or be in a position to rent an apartment to meet your needs. That is the sure way to keep your self-respect and retain your precious independence.

## 2. WHERE WILL YOU LIVE?

Do your future plans include moving to some other city or state? Have you been thinking of going to Arizona, Colorado, Florida or California? What do you know about that area? Are you basing your choice on the fact that you spent one or two vacations there? Have you been there at other times of the year? Have you visualized it not as a tourist impressed with the various show places but as one of the residents? What is the town or city like in the spring, in the summer, in the winter, in the rainy seasons?

Take a leave of absence from your job, if possible, and spend some time there. If you cannot do it, subscribe to the local newspaper, get the chamber of commerce reports and other pertinent business details. If you belong to a union, a trade organization or a fraternal order, to a service group or a given church denomination, ask for specific details from the secretary of the group or from the spiritual leader, and analyze their replies in the light of day.

There are many things to be considered before you break old ties, sell your home, dispose of your personal effects and transplant yourself to some far-off place. Even when you are set on the particular area, you may find it more advisable to live in one of the suburbs rather than in the heart of the city. It may be better for you in a dozen different ways.

And, if you are planning to purchase a home there, you have to be doubly sure and careful. How will it serve your needs when older age creeps up on you? For instance, if the bedrooms are upstairs, climbing steps later on may be difficult or dangerous for you. If it is too far from shopping or transportation, too close to heavy traffic, or has other drawbacks which you are willing to overlook now, how will it be when infirmities or disabilities come your way? This does not imply that you should think of the house you are going to buy as a rest home but as a place suitable for older people.

Of course, your financial status and your present medical history will also have a strong bearing upon the place you choose and the house you buy. Supposing you have to work part time to supplement your income? What does that town or locality have in possible employment for you? Will the climate through the entire year, or the elevation, or the job potentials be in keeping with what you want and need?

What provisions are there for medical care, for transportation to and from a medical center, for church affiliations, for communal life, for being part of the activities around you? Are there any restrictions or limitations which may affect you, directly or indirectly? Will you be readily accepted or remain an outsider? What allowances or sacrifices would you have to make so as to belong and become part of the community?

If you do not have the right answers to these and other similar questions, begin to check into it carefully and most thoroughly. Better still, if your retirement is only a short time away and the plan is feasible for you, sublease your home for the time being and go to the place you selected as your future home to live there for a while. Assume that you are already one of the permanent residents there and learn at firsthand whether or not living there will be just as you pictured it to be. Make sure you are not chasing a will-o-the-wisp. You cannot afford to take the risk and burn your bridges behind you.

In your younger days, when you moved from one place to another, it did not affect you too much. Now, with older age upon you, you have to be more careful before you try to transplant yourself.

Some states have special provisions for older adults— Arizona, California, Florida, Oregon, Washington, to mention only five of them. But whatever those provision or conveniences are, moving may be too much for you. This is especially true, if you happen to be set in your ways, do not mix readily with others or cannot adapt yourself too readily to new places and conditions. You may be too miserable in the new surroundings no matter how much better they are than what you left behind. Some people are too unhappy when they have to leave old friends behind. You may be one of them.

### 3. Your Home and Your Personal Effects

If you own your home and intend to move elsewhere, what about your house? Would you be better off to sell it or to keep it? Would it be wise to let a child take it over? This is not much of a problem if there is only one child. But if you have several, you have to have the wisdom of a Solomon to know what to do and what child shall move into your home. Any choice you make may be the wrong one. Would you do better if you were to lease your house to a stranger? If so, what should the lease call for and should your furniture and furnishings be included? If, on the other hand, you intend to dispose of your home, will you be buying another house elsewhere and what will you do in the meantime?

All of these and similar things have to be given due consideration long before you "take the plunge" and decide to sell your house, to rent it or to let a child live there.

There is also the question of your personal effects which you accumulated through the years. Many of them have special sentimental values to you but are worthless to someone else. "Staying put" where you are, those things are not in your way but should you decide to move elsewhere and cart them along with you they may become both a burden and a liability. They may involve needless worries and expenses for you and make living elsewhere much more difficult and troublesome.

### 4. YOUR FUTURE INCOME

What will your future income be? Do you know how much you will receive in social security payments or in returns from your own investments, from a retirement pension or from old age assistance? Will your moving to another state affect any of the payments to you? Will your total income be sufficient to take care of your needs and expectant medical expenses? Would you have to supplement your income in other ways?

What steps will you be taking to adapt your standard of living to your eventual reduced income? Would you have to retrench and perhaps scrimp all along the way? With such prospects before you, you may not want to remain in the same locality or in the same city. You may decide to move away and live among strangers so as not to have to apologize to anyone or be self-conscious about your reduced circumstances.

### 5. YOUR FUTURE ACTIVITIES

If you are working for someone and know that you will not be allowed to stay on after you reach 65, it may be important for you, at this time, to put in as much extra time as you can and thus build up your nest egg. On the other hand, if you feel that your subsequent income will be sufficient for your future needs, you may be wise in your decision to slow down, to relinquish some of your duties and responsibilities now and gradually get used to the idea of not working at all.

If your job entails special skills and you are asked to

train others to "step into your shoes," that may hold special significance for you, because if your employer is willing to pay you to teach others you may find it profitable later on to do the same on a private basis and on your own time. That would provide you with a ready job after your retirement to suit your wishes and circumstances. And, if the training calls for equipment or machinery, it might pay you to make the investment or join forces with others, younger than you, and start a training school which could conceivably become an accredited institution.

If you are working for yourself and put in too many hours at work, begin to delegate some of your responsibilities to others. Take extra time off, mornings, afternoons or at the end of each week. Teach others how to handle the manual, the technical, the tiring details, while you devote more and more time to administrative and supervisory activities.

Then, as your retirement age draws nearer, start passing on the executive responsibilities as well, so that you would be free to come in only occasionally, to leave on lengthy trips and eventually relinquish all cares, duties and responsibilities.

## 6. Your Recreations

Use the free time you take off, whether working for others or for yourself, to acquire new contacts, new interests and activities. If you have been working with your hands, try to cultivate an artistic or cultural activity. Learn how to paint, to sing, to write, to compose, to play an instrument or do something else in the creative fields to bring you a new sense of accomplishment. And while doing so, do not expect to became a famous artist, writer or musician. Find pleasure in doing those things for their sake.

If, on the other hand, you followed intellectual or scientific pursuits as part of your daily work, learn to make something with your hands. Let it be an activity which calls for mental coordination, for a sense of balance or color complement, for rhythm or special timing, for symmetry or proper perspective. Let it be handwork in wood or metal, in clay or mosaics, in pen or crayon, in cloth or wire, in die or tool work, in mechanics or arrangement. It is surprising how much pleasure such activity can bring to one who never fashioned anything with his hands.

## 7. Periodic Checkups

If you have been active in sports and are past your fiftieth birthday, begin to restrict yourself and cut down on all sport activities which lead to physical exertion.

You have, no doubt, had the experience of noticing how a car, even a new one, will often labor in climbing a hill. The experienced driver keeps that in mind and to avoid needless strain on the engine or perhaps stall along the way he usually shifts from high gear to medium or low. This becomes all the more important as the car grows older.

You, too, are a composite of many mechanical and muscular organisms, and whether old or young place extra stress on your heart, lungs, muscles and various organs when indulging in strenuous sports. As you grow older your various muscles and organs cannot respond so readily, so effortlessly, as before. So, do not subject yourself needlessly to extra strain and exertions. Slow down a bit. Change to second or low gear, as it were. Take things slower, easier, even if you feel "fit as a fiddle" and can seemingly go on at the same pace you did years ago, without any apparent ill effects.

Do this on your own cognizance. Better still, begin to take periodic medical checkups. Let your doctor tell you when and where to draw the line on sport activities and on many of the other things you do. It is sure to save you needless pain, prevent sickness and add years to your life. Start doing it now, before you retire.

## 8. EMOTIONAL STABILITY

Begin to cultivate a realistic sense of values. Study, learn and adopt ways that will tend to make you self-sufficient in many respects and thus release you from full dependence upon others. This will surely add to your emotional stability in your later years.

For instance, as a married woman who always depended upon her husband to take care of all business and financial matters, you may lose him somewhere along the way before you both reach your retirement age. You may be forced to take over suddenly and be at a loss to know what to do and how to carry on. So, begin to prepare yourself for such eventuality. Start doing it gradually, *now*. Begin to handle the household bills. Become familiar with your husband's work or profession, especially with the financial end of it. Know all you need to know about his insurance policies and his investments as well as the various obligations he assumed for himself, for you or for others. If he is in business begin to take an active part in it, *now*. Learn all that you would have to know if he were suddenly taken from you and the responsibility to carry on in his place were to fall upon you.

If you are a man nearing your retirement age, who never paid much attention to the mechanics of homekeeping, who left such matters to your wife and let her care for you and take care of all personal things, better take stock and realize that she may be gone before her time and you may be forced to carry on alone for a while. With this in mind, start doing little things for yourself at home. Learn to do many of the little personal chores. Learn how to prepare a simple meal and how to handle ordinary household chores.

## 9. The Physical Marks of Older Age

Whether or not you are ready to admit it, age is gradually leaving its visible manifestations upon you. Prepare yourself for them, mentally and emotionally. If your hair is turning gray, if your sight or hearing is losing its sharpness, if you are not so spry and quick to respond to stimuli as you used to do, and if you can no longer be so casual about food, drink or sleep, do not take it to heart. Do not start fighting your age or worry needlessly. Do not assume it means the beginning of the end for you and start "burning the candle at both ends." There will be many good, happy, healthy years for you to enjoy life in its many forms, provided you go sensibly about things and plan properly for the days to come.

## 10. Your Changing Status

Begin to accept your changing status as an older person with equanimity and do not berate the younger people who look down upon you or start treating you as someone old. When you were in your teens any person past thirty or thirty-five years of age was "old" to you, and anyone past that age was an "ancient one" to you.

You looked upon yourself as the embodiment of the "new look," the new generation, as the one with the most modern advanced ideas and plans. How could anyone in his forties or his fifties possibly see, understand, appreciate and visualize the bright glorious future ahead? How could anyone of such age grasp your scope of change, your youthful approach, your dreams of things to come? That basic difference between the young and the old has never changed and it is as true today as it was in your youth.

As for aping the young in their dress, speech, manners and behavior and thus pretend that you are still one of them is foolhardy. The young will shun you and those in your age group will pity you and laugh at you behind your back. And, if you insist on carrying on that make-believe it is bound to affect you both physically and mentally. So, be your age and act your age. There is dignity and respect in age. There is maturity of judgment and a realistic sense of values. Capitalize upon them. Put them to good use and let them add stature to your contact with the young.

## 11. Growing With Older Age

Do not begrudge the passing of time or bewail the advent of a new birthday. Be glad you are growing older. Grow with your new age as day passes day and brings you new opportunities to live and enjoy life. Grow with the years in new outlooks on life, in new contacts, in new interests, and in the diversity of your interests. Grow with the years in tolerance and in understanding, in compassion and goodness of heart. It will repay you in hundreds of ways and make people glad to be with you and near you.

Start making your plans early enough so as to be able to enjoy fully the coming "age of appreciation." To paraphrase a passage from "How to Conquer Fears, Worries and Frustrations in 30 Hours," ". . . The secret of remaining young at an older age lies not in looks or contours, in social or sport activities, in pretense or make-believe, but in the way you think and act. Aging begins when you settle down to a sedentary animalistic existence, when you allow yourself to vegetate, when you lose interest in everything else but food, sleep, comforts and the constant reference to the pains you have and the operations you had . . ."

## 12. New Interests

Develop a sense of pride and a feeling of accomplishment in the new interests you are acquiring. Cultivate your "bump of curiosity" and start asking questions about many of the things which you have been taking for granted through the years. Look for the right answers in books, magazines and the studies you undertake. Widen your visions, broaden your concepts and learn to derive a greater measure of enjoyment and satisfaction from the ordinary, simple doings of each day. You may be forced to eliminate some of your old-time favorite pursuits but there is nothing tragic about it, so long as you replace them with others which may prove to be more satisfying and gratifying.

## 13. Follow Your Skills and Inclinations

There is no one, anywhere, exactly like you. You have certain talents, abilities and aptitudes which you, and you alone, can utilize and develop. Perhaps they have been dormant through the years or perhaps you have never given yourself much credit for knowing what you know or doing the things you do so well.

If those talents have lain dormant start looking for them now. You will find them in your special bents and inclinations. You will recognize them in the added interest you show in some given topic or activity. You will know them in the ease with which you can handle certain tasks or the sense of satisfaction you get when you do something you enjoy doing. Whatever it be, give it room to grow. Devote time and effort to it even when others are ready to deride your attempt and belittle your efforts. What others might say or think does not count so long as you derive pleasure and satisfaction therefrom, so long as you are doing what brings you a sense of well-being and accomplishment.

If you have been doing something extremely well, look into its possibilities as a marketable part-time employment. It may be playing bridge, managing recalcitrant children, handling animals, cultivating flowers, knitting garments, baking pies, making goodies, canning preserves, fixing appliances, decorating interiors, telling stories, doing caricatures, composing ditties, devising games or being easy on your feet.

Whatever it be, try to visualize it as something you can do for others, as something you can teach to others. Check into its sales possibilities now, while you are still working and can treat it purely as a hobby or a pastime. Talk with people who deal in such products or services. Experiment with it on a small scale in your spare time. Make believe you have to depend upon it for your livelihood and learn at firsthand what it would require to turn that ability, hobby or special skill, into a paying activity.

Many a bigtime business of today was started in that way. The special skill or ability which you have been taking for granted may prove to be an absorbing full-time or part-time occupation in the golden years to come and add much to your joys of living.

This could easily become the beginning of a new life for

you, an interesting life replete with health-promoting activities to make you glad that you have reached an age when you can indulge your dreams and be all important to yourself and to others.

## 14. SELF-SUFFICIENCY

Begin to cultivate a sense of self-reliance and self-sufficiency. Do not doubt your capacity to learn and to change. Be ready and willing to stand on your own feet and trust your inner judgment, when in the privacy of your own heart you feel that you are right. Learn how to be self-sufficient and get along with yourself, steadfast in your sincere beliefs and able to enjoy your natural gifts while in your own company.

Nearly two thousand years ago Lucius Seneca, the philosopher, said: "Watch over yourself. Be your own accuser, then your judge; ask yourself grace sometimes, and, if there is need, impose upon yourself some pain."

You can learn to be self-reliant and self-sufficient, but that takes time. Start now and you will be able to benefit by these important attributes when you are ready to retire.

## 15. NEW FRIENDS

Friendships cannot be built overnight. They take time, effort, application, cultivation, and call for many qualities that can be cultivated.

Among them are consideration, helpfulness, affability, neighborliness, cheerfulness, cooperation, an unselfish attitude and a readiness to overlook minor failings. Among them are also sympathy, patience, loyalty, discretion, tolerance, generosity and goodness of heart. All of these can be developed and acquired, if you so desire.

Do not expect to find anyone without faults. No one is or can be expected to be perfect or infallible. All human beings have their failings and even the most capable among us has his shortcomings and makes seemingly glaring and foolish mistakes now and then. Be willing to accept others as they are and do not try to make them over to suit you. Be also willing to step back and take "second place" from time to time so as to give someone else the chance to shine. This is one of the surest ways to make friends.

Old friends are hard to "come by" and are priceless. Do not push the old aside just because you made new friends. The old can be a true blessing to you in your older age because with them you can share old pleasures and memories. Old friends span the gap of time, bring the past into the present and thus help you to maintain and retain established contacts and happy relationships.

## 16. Be Willing to Change

One of the important things to learn, before you retire, is to know how to bend with the need and avoid becoming set in your ways. You have to cultivate the ability to change courses if need be, to acclimate yourself to pending changes in thought, in concept, in behavior and in keeping with new trends and developments as they affect you in the bosom of your family and in your contacts with other people.

Visualize your coming retirement not as a calamity but as something you have been waiting for, as a new phase in your journey through life, as a stepping stone to better things, as the opportunity to stop working for a living and begin to indulge your whims and follow the things you wanted to do.

## 17. PART-TIME WORK

If you know now that your future income will not be
sufficient to meet your needs, begin to accumulate a little extra
each payday if possible or start looking for part-time work to
follow after you retire. Begin with an analysis of your present job or occupation. Is there anything about what you do
now that you could utilize later, away from its present set-
up and existing facilities? Does your job, the product or the
service, have within itself, within its component parts or
within closely allied fields, some small item or service which
you could handle later, on a small scale and on a part-
time basis?

Would such work come within the scope of your age,
knowledge, ability, financial means and possible physical disabilities? Could you work at it with the help of a stranger or
with some member of the family who would carry the brunt
of the details? Would you have a ready outlet for the product
or the service, without heavy involvements in stock, equipment or other overhead expenses? If so, start working at it
now. Do it during your spare moments, on evenings or weekends. Do it with someone who is trustworthy and could handle
all the tiresome details. Then, as the plan takes hold, start
giving more time to it so as to put it on a firm basis and later
on enable you to retire TO a business of your own.

## 18. YOUR HEALTH

One of the important factors in your ability to do the
things you would like to do and thus fully enjoy your retirement will be the status of your health. This is something you
cannot and must not ignore, and the time to start paying more
attention to your health is, *now.*

Begin with a complete diagnostic checkup. Let your medical examination be as thorough as if you were applying for a million dollars worth of life insurance. Let your doctor check particularly the possible inroads of metabolic, arthritic, tumorous and vascular system diseases.

One of the things to watch is overweight. You may have to change your habits of eating, cut out rich, spicy food and double helpings of desserts and use more proteins. As a matter of fact, all of your habits may have to be looked into and some of them may be best to eliminate entirely. This is where the advice of your doctor will count. Listen to him and follow his advice rather than some food faddist who happens to be popular for the moment.

## 19. New Studies

Take up something new, in some special field. Do not put too much stock in the old notion that an old dog cannot be taught new tricks. This is not so. The hundreds of graduating students in adult education classes throughout the country, year after year, have dispelled that mistaken belief long ago.

A person past fifty may find it harder to concentrate. He may have to unlearn certain things before learning something new but he can surely take his rightful place among students of any age. You are no exception. If you so desire, you can take up the study of any subject and even become an authority in that field.

It is never too late to learn something new, never too late to acquire new interests and make new friends. Take advantage of all the opportunities you have now to prepare for happier living later, and then when your retirement comes you will be ready to enjoy it.

## 20. WORKING WITH OTHERS

Retirement is your second chance to live a rewarding and satisfying life in your later years, but to be able to do it properly you must prepare yourself and plan ahead of time. Retirement calls for a new sense of values and a new approach to everyday living.

If you are working for a firm where there are others of your age who should be preparing themselves for their retirement, ask the management for permission to start classes in preparation for retirement. Then get in touch with your local school board, your social welfare agencies, and your county or state Committee on Aging. They could arrange to have a gerontologist or a trained social service worker conduct classes to help you and your group in your preretirement studies.

The instructor will help you evaluate your abilities and capitalize upon your background and experience in preparing for the leisure years to come. He will help you arrange your finances, take better care of your health and set the pace for the days to follow, when you retire from active work in one field to some other activities. He will show you how to discover new ways to be useful to yourself and to others and how to take full advantage of the opportunities for personal achievement and satisfaction.

The twenty steps suggested for your preretirement program are not all-inclusive. Add your own ideas to the suggestions given and let them become your stepping stones to your eventual retirement. Then you will surely be on the way to better, brighter and richer days, and be better equipped to find the gold in your golden age.

# CHAPTER TWO

# The Benefits of Older Age

The privilege granted to you to reach your present age was denied to many others, to those who are already gone and to those younger than you who shall never reach your present age. So, be glad you can grow older. Be thankful and grateful for the years you have already lived and for the good days yet to come. They can be rewarding years, the best years, the most enjoyable years.

It is within your power to make your older age really worth-while, regardless of your sex, your background, your looks or your economic status. It is within your power to put to good use all of your unused, untapped potentialities, to develop a wider range of interests and to benefit by all the opportunities modern living offers you.

You are now free to start anew, to rectify old mistakes, to try your hand at different things, to follow your particular inclinations and use your free time to add to your enjoyments and to your accomplishments. Life in the past may not have been too good to you. Perhaps you had to work at something you did not like. You kept at it only because you had obligations to meet, because you dared not experiment with other work or jobs lest you fall behind in your earnings and fail to provide for those who were dependent upon you for their support.

Now, all of that is behind you. You have a new chance, your second chance, to leave the "old" behind and within the limitations of your age and capacities, do what you always wanted to do, start a new career if you so desire, rediscover yourself, and turn old dreams into a reality.

You have been waiting for many years to reach the time in life when you could start all over again, when you could follow a given field without having to consider the loss in earnings or the obligations to your family. This is no time for you to fret or to worry, to be sick or lonely, and if there is nothing you care to study at the moment begin to build friendships. Begin to take an interest in people around you and get to know them.

Every person you meet, whoever he might be, is like a new book, filled with surprising situations and denouements. He is a living book, with page after page and chapter after chapter of absorbing incidents and developments. What is more, the story is still unfolding. Many pages are still to be written, pages replete with drama, action, suspense, conflict and triumphs yet to be reached. You can have a hand in those developments and what joy you could get by being one of the characters, one of the makers of new interesting and desirable situations.

Life around you can be so gratifying, so satisfying, especially if you take an active part in it and expose yourself to people and things. Your years of living have given you knowledge, wisdom, experience, good judgment. Put them to good use for yourself and for others, and particularly for those who need encouragement.

Do not take it for granted that because you are old or because you have limited means you cannot help others. Your age may be an added asset and those in need of help may not be looking for financial support. Perhaps all they want is advice or someone to listen. The mere fact that you are ready and willing to listen may be enough. So—let people come to you with their woes and troubles. Lend them your ears and be pleasant about it. Be sympathetic and understanding even when what they confide to you is boring and childish.

Do these things graciously and before long those who come to you with their woes and their problems will also want to share with you some of their joys and triumphs. That is sure to bring you many moments of joy and satisfaction, add to your sense of accomplishment and build ever-growing, lasting friendships.

Your past is behind you and the less you regurgitate the mistakes and the unpleasant happenings of yesterday the better for you. Remember not to repeat the same mistakes today, but beyond that let the past fade into what "was" and look forward to the things you can do today. Tomorrow is still far away. You cannot tell what it might bring, yet it is safe to say that, insofar as general conditions are concerned, your tomorrow will be as empty and as colorless as today, unless you take steps *now*, to improve your time, *today*.

Remember that even the longest journey begins with a single step. So, take the initial step now to make today count. Take the first step now to improve your mind, to replace harmful habits, to widen your interests, to make new friends and to enjoy the simple things all around you.

Let your first step be a proper evaluation and appreciation of all the comforts and conveniences at your command.

For instance, do you realize that you have greater powers right now than any king or monarch of old? Even Aladdin with his magic lamp could hardly summon so many genii to do his bidding. Those genii are all around you. You need only summon them and they will hurry to obey you, at any time and at all times.

Those servants are always ready to answer your call and do what you ask them to do, without protest or reservations. You will find them in buttons, in discs, in dials and switches all around you. Push one of those buttons on the wall near you and the genie imprisoned there will rush through your house to flood it with light. Push another button and the genie behind it will rush to cool you or to warm you.

Twirl a mounted dial on a small contraption near you several times and the genie hidden there will race hundreds of miles across space and within seconds bring to your ears the voice of someone you want to hear, although the two of you may be many miles apart. Turn the knobs on a small or some-what larger cabinet beside you and the genie therein will hasten to speed across thousands of miles to bring music to your ears. Change the knob's position by turning it to the left or to the right and new voices will come your way. You will be tuned to a song or a play or to the eye-account of an event transpiring at the very moment miles and miles away.

Turn the dials on another contrivance in your home and several genii working in unison will enable you not only to hear what goes on elsewhere but also to see what happens as it is happening, although you and the event are hundreds of miles apart. Twist the same dials slightly to the left or to the right and new events will come your way, from some other far-off place.

Step into the modern version of a "magic carpet" and it

will soar into the skies and carry you across limitless space, across land and sea, to any part of the world. Step into the earthbound version of a similar "magic carpet" and with the turn of a switch bring hundreds of sleeping horses to life. They will respond to your slightest wish and sprint across miles of land, over hill and dale, through sleeping roads or streets teeming with life, to take you to any destination you desire.

Push buttons, press pedals, twist knobs, flip switches, turn dials, insert plugs or connect wires and hundreds of genii will come to attention, eager to do whatever you ask. They will open doors, close windows, start fires, cook meals, chill water, wash clothes, cool the air, sweep floors, snap pictures, start talking or singing, take notes, record your voice, guard your valuables and do numerous jobs for you at home, at work, at play or wherever you happen to be at any time. They will do it every time, all the time, without ever tiring or complaining.

Does all of this sound fantastic? Perhaps in the way it is being told at the moment, but it is true. The only reason why it does not startle you is because it is part of your daily living and you have been taking it as a matter of course. But, just for the fun of it, take a little time out now to list on a sheet of paper all the electrical gadgets and appliances you put to use during the day and evening at home, at work, at play.

Enumerate them one by one. Try to picture them as if you have never seen them and never used them before, and your amazement will grow from minute to minute. Try to visualize them as if you were someone who lived several hundred years ago and was brought back to life for this one day, as one who is given the opportunity to put all those servants to work for the very first time, and you will readily agree that you have more genii at your command than Aladdin.

At the same time, keep this salient fact in mind, you listed only the common electrical appliances in ordinary use. But what about the many new and hitherto unknown genii pressed into service for your comfort and benefit during recent years? What about the X-ray machines, the photocell, the movies, the sonic and radar apparatus and all the other ways in which electronics are made to serve you? And what about the atomic age with its corps of genii that are being introduced into your life and promise to do so much to make your life richer and brighter?

All of those things and many more are yours to use and to enjoy. The great, big, wide, wonderful world, with all of man's shortcomings, is beautiful to live in, wonderful to behold. It is yours to benefit by if only you keep your age in mind, live sensibly and do not ape youth in your habits, efforts and activities.

Be aware of your restriction and wear your age proudly. Take pride in the fact that you have weathered different stages in life and take comfort in your maturity. Pay little attention to those who might claim that you are too old for this or that. Do not try to justify yourself in the eyes of the younger generations.

It is true that you can no longer compete with youth in those sport activities where physical endurance, speed in reaction and muscular effort are the dominant factors. Let youth glory in those things while you capitalize upon your matured age.

There are certain limitations inherent in older age but, strangely enough, every age has its own peculiar drawbacks and shortcomings. The child is entirely dependent upon its parents, the teen-ager is limited by his lack of knowledge and experience and must rely upon his elders even when he claims to be self-sufficient, the young adult is burdened with learning to make a living, with the cares of a growing family and with the needs to provide for his later years.

You, on the other hand, have already passed through those stages in your life. You have now reached your golden age, the age of appreciation, the age of understanding, the age of leisurely living. All the years that came before were simply the preparation for the present moment, to make the most of every opportunity and fully enjoy day-to-day living.

If you do not have to work part-time to supplement your income, turn your pastimes into vocations as well as avocations. If you have certain skills, teach them to others. Do it on a free basis or at a nominal fee geared to your needs and desires. If you feel that things in your town are not run properly, go into politics or form civic groups to combat the existing situations. If you have no particular causes to espouse or special skills to teach others and would like to do something for your community, volunteer to work for any civic agency and you will be welcomed with open arms.

If you are undecided as to where you could be of greater use, get in touch with your nearest hospital, community center, church, fraternal order, service organization or senior citizen group. They will be glad to direct your efforts and help you find something to do, something rewarding and satisfying.

Be sure, however, not to become overenthusiastic and go overboard on any activity. Your age puts certain limitations upon you and it would be foolhardy to place needless strains upon your physical and nervous systems.

What are some of the ways to take better care of yourself? Here are a few of them:

1—Have periodic health examinations. Place yourself in the hands of a geriatrician and let him set the pace for your conduct and behavior. He will help you guard against the inroads of chronic and degenerative diseases and minimize or arrest their possible effects upon you.

2—Watch your food intake. Avoid heavy, rich, fat foods. Eat slowly, sparingly, and above all watch your weight. It is easy to put on extra pounds but it is considerably harder to take them off afterwards. Be sensible in your choice of food and do not go in for diets or become a faddist. Use a diet only when your doctor prescribes it and do not take up any regimen because some glib advertising approaches happen to appeal to you or impress you for the moment.

3—Be fully aware of the bad habits you have and how harmful they may be to your well-being. This is especially important when your doctor tells you to restrict or to discontinue doing certain things. Habits can be changed or replaced and you would be wise to follow your doctor's counsel and his admonitions.

4—If you have been following certain sport activities that tend to tire you now, drop them. Do not waste your physical and nervous energies needlessly. Above all, avoid petty irritations and minor disagreements. They can become your implacable enemies. Follow a certain activity only so long as it brings you pleasure or relaxation. Stop doing whatever it is, the moment it starts to master you or becomes a tiring chore.

5—Take your age and your growing limitations in your stride. Minimize the effects of minor ailments and discomforts and do not allow them to dominate your feelings and reactions. If you have to wear glasses, use a hearing aid, be more careful in climbing stairs or restrict yourself in some other way, where is the tragedy? Many men and women, much younger than you, have to contend with similar or more serious limitations and still manage to lead full, useful and enjoyable lives.

6—Accept the changes within and around you without resentments. Do not bemoan the encroachment of age and fight it all the way. You cannot possibly win. Change with the need and the times and begin breaking down preconceived notions right now. Avoid becoming set in your ways and refusing to budge from entrenched beliefs, for they lead to accelerated "aging" in mind and in body. Look for the good in everything. Be willing to try out the new. You may like it much better than you anticipate and it is bound to keep you young at heart.

7—Cultivate peace of mind and let the petty annoyances of the day pass you by. Refuse to make an issue of little indignities which may come your way or become incensed because others are thoughtless or indifferent. Have a high regard for your sincere convictions but do not turn them into a club or a crutch to lean upon. Establish a sense of values for yourself and let them guide you in choosing friends, in following various activities and utilizing your leisure time.

Follow these basic steps in maintaining a sane, sensible, healthy attitude toward life and make the most of every opportunity to enjoy life. Then as surely as the sun shall rise again and again, you will find more pleasures and contentment in your golden age.

# CHAPTER THREE

# What Are Your Common Fears?

George Harmon was a dress designer and in keeping with union rules and Social Security regulations had to quit at age 65, although he was in good health and could have continued doing as good a job for several more years.

He had given little thought to retirement, in former years. He was too busy working on the job he liked, taking care of home expenses even after his children were married, paying off his mortgage and maintaining his social position to worry about that far-off day when he would retire.

But when that day came it "hit" him hard. George tried to argue with his employer, with the business agent and with all others who would listen, but to no avail. And so, accepting his enforced retirement as a temporary stoppage of work, he rejoiced for a while in his new freedom.

The jobless days passed into weeks and soon staying in bed an extra hour or two, reading the paper, sitting in the park, watching TV or playing pinochle three times a week began to pall on George. He tried to get his old job back, he tried to come in as a cutter, as a stock boy, and work for one half of his old salary, but his age was against him. He tried other places and towns and met with the same answer—you are too old.

George had to do something. So, he began to interfere with his wife's chores and meddle in the lives of his children. They did not take kindly to it and it started arguments. This led to estrangements and resentments. He took it all to heart and it brought higher blood pressure, heart palpitations, sleeplessness and digestive disturbances.

George went to see the family doctor and was told to rest, to relax, to take things easy, to enjoy his retirement. It infuriated him. He went to other doctors who could find nothing wrong with him. He had to prove to himself and to others that such was not the case and soon something in him answered the call. His blood pressure went up, his heart developed palpitations, his kidneys stopped functioning properly and his digestive system went "out of whack."

To make things worse, George's mental attitude toward himself and those around him also changed. He began to feel that his family wanted to get rid of him, that his friends shunned him, that he was of no use to anyone anymore, that nothing but pain and misery was in store for him and that he might as well be dead, if not in a natural way, then by his own hand. This made him a psychosomatic casualty.

Lillian Stengel was head buyer of children's wear for the Roger chain of department stores and lost none of her abilities when she reached her 65th birthday. Yet because of company rules and Social Security regulations she was forced to quit her important and lucrative job.

She was a career woman and through the years gave little thought to the day when she would have to retire. Somehow she thought of herself as being indispensable, that she could retain her position as long as she wanted. Millions of dollars went through her hands year after year and no one ever questioned her judgment.

She was used to being "looked up" to, to being feted and dined by salesmen and manufacturers, to being treated like a queen whenever she went on buying trips and to having her ideas and comments readily accepted. She met many eligible men in the course of her work and some of them proposed to her. But she could not see herself giving up all she enjoyed for the dubious role of housewife, and as the years passed the thought of marrying someone was pushed further and further aside.

And suddenly there was nothing. . . . A single change in the calendar year was enough to place her among the old, the useless, the unemployed, the unwanted. It struck her like a bolt from the blue. Her mirror did not show much of a change. She saw to it a few years earlier. The proper hair dye, the face lift during a buying trip, the right foundation garments, the skillful make-up, the night and morning exercises, and eating sparingly of fattening foods. All of this kept her looking slim, trim and attractive. No one could possibly judge her to be more than fifty or fifty-two. But her birth certificate and the Social Security records gave her true age and there was nothing she could do about it.

She was not worried so much about having food to eat and a roof over her head. She saved a little, had a few shares of stock in the Roger Company, had a pension coming and Social Security benefits. But the total was hardly enough to maintain the same quarters and live in the free style to which she had grown accustomed. She had to cut quickly, drastically, and suddenly fears began to assail her.

What if she took sick and had a major hospital bill to pay out of her own pocket? How long would her nest egg last and how could she replenish it? What if she suffered a major sense impairment or grew disabled and needed someone to take care of her? To whom could she turn for help, when she had no relatives and no husband to care for her? If she was too old to work now, what chance would she have to find work several years later if she had to go to work? What chances did she have now to meet the right man and what had she to offer him? What should she do with her spare time? Dare she take the risk to open a shop in some neighborhood and compete with the giants in the field? Supposing she did open a place of her own and then took sick or became disabled?

The more Lillian brooded over these things the greater grew her fears and the more despondent she became. It began to tell on her. She lost weight and developed strange, mysterious ailments. She went to see her doctor. He gave her pills. They did not help. She went to another doctor and before long she, too, became a psychsomatic casualty.

George Hamon's case and Lillian Stengel's breakdown are typical examples of the lack of preparation for one's retirement and some of the fears common to older age.

Among those fears may be: 1) The fear of being or remaining alone in your older age. 2) The fear of growing old and feeble. 3) The fear of getting sick or being disabled. 4) The fear of dying or losing someone dear to you. 5) The fear of becoming a burden to others. 6) The fear of suffering impairments or disabilities. 7) The fear of having nothing to do. 8) The fear of being useless and unwanted. 9) The fear of new and strange conditions.

Let us examine those fears one by one. Let us expose them to the light of day and learn how to cope with them.

## 1. THE FEAR OF BEING OR REMAINING ALONE

This fear is most prevalent among those who lost a spouse recently and have had little time to adjust themselves to life without a mate. There is the feeling of being forsaken. The spouse is missed not only because there may have been a deep love or an attachment, but because he was part and parcel of their long life together. With the spouse gone there is a void which no one else can fill for the time being. It is an emptiness which turns into loneliness and grows into a mounting fear.

The older couple who spent many years of their lives to raise a family feel very much alone when their children marry and start homes of their own. The sudden stillness in the house and the seeming emptiness of the days ahead frighten them. For a while, when the children are first married, the old folks try to retain the "old-time" hold. They use different subterfuges to be closer to the children, to have a hand in the plans and the activities of the youngsters. But as time goes on they realize that their advice and admonitions, their ideas and suggestions, are often overlooked and at times deliberately ignored. This has an adverse effect upon the old couple and their fears grow.

There are times in the life of every person, young as well as old, when one stands alone and must walk alone most of the way. Sickness, pain, grief, sorrow, heartache, shattered dreams and disappointments come his way. They cannot be passed along or shared with others. Friends and relatives may sympathize or commiserate. They may express it in

words and in suitable action. But deep in one's heart the pain
or the hurt, the sorrow or the anguish, the heartache or the
bitter disappointment still remain, and one must find the
strength within himself to carry on.

There are also other times in the life of man, and the
older person may often take it as a personal affront, when
because of a sickness or an accident there is a serious sense
impairment or a permanent disability, and he must stand
alone for a while. His friends and family may sympathize
and offer different consolations, but nothing can ease the feeling of futility, the effects of the loss. Then one must look for
strength and courage from within until such time when self-
confidence is regained and the determination to carry on is
strengthened.

Of course, all of these misfortunes can happen to anyone
at any time, to the young as well as the old. Pain, sorrow,
grief, troubles, sickness, accidents or disabling injuries can
come upon all of us. They have no regard for age, sex, time,
place, circumstance or one's station in life. Yet the old take
it more to heart when it happens to them.

As for loneliness, it is primarily a state of mind, a self-
induced mental attitude that can be dissipated. You will never
be alone, in the simple meaning of the term, so long as you
mingle with people and take part in their activities. You will
never be alone, no matter what your sex, age, background or
station in life are, so long as you meet people part of the
way or all of the way, when it is desirable. You will never
be alone so long as you keep busy doing something you
like or learned to like. You will never be lonely so long as
you are friendly, cheerful, amiable and cooperative, and
are willing to carry your share of the load, especially when
it is not expected of you. You will never be lonely so long as

you make others feel free "to be themselves" in your company.

## 2. THE FEAR OF GROWING OLD AND FEEBLE

The terms "old" and "feeble" have nothing in common. Old age has no monopoly on feebleness, and feebleness, meaning poor health, does not imply old age. Poor health, whether of a physical or mental nature, can affect anyone, the old and the young, in all walks of life, regardless of time, place or family status.

Of course, there are many older men and women who are sick, infirm, bedridden and even senile. But by the same token there are thousands of young men and women who are crippled, physically or mentally, who shall never fully recover and never lead healthy, normal lives.

Do not saddle yourself with the fear of growing older. To reach his older age is the dream and the hope of every young person living today, no matter how difficult the journey ahead. You were no exception to this universal desire. You worked, planned, strived and saved for the days to come when you could take life leisurely and enjoy your sunset years.

Now that those days are here make the most of them. Be glad you reached your present age. Be glad that you can talk, walk, see, hear, learn, listen, work, play and participate in the activities that appeal to you. And even if you are limited in some way and cannot do all the things you would like to do, make the most of what you have, of what you are, of what you CAN do.

## 3. THE FEAR OF SICKNESS OR OF DISABILITIES

The mere fact that you are afraid or that you worry too much about the eventuality of being sick or becoming disabled will not prevent its happening. The advancing years carry with them certain ailments, discomforts and impairments which cannot be stopped or prevented in any way.

Among them may be poorer vision, impaired hearing, poorer blood circulation, shortness of breath, inability to stay up nights or follow favorite sport activities and a host of minor organic disorders. There may also be the initial onset of degenerative older age ailments which can be minimized by following a doctor's advice.

Whatever they might be, some of them can be prevented and others cannot. Some arthritic, metabolic and tumorous conditions can be stopped or arrested, but other ailments will follow as the natural sequences of aging. All of this must be looked upon in a realistic manner and what is inevitable must be accepted with grace and equanimity. Your mental attitude has a great deal to do with the way you accept the inevitable and learn to live with it day after day.

## 4. The Fear of Dying or Losing Someone Dear to You

As you grow older and some of your friends, relatives, or people you know pass away, you begin to worry. You find yourself bidding the last farewell to someone who was close to you, someone of your own age or perhaps younger, someone who seemed to be in better health than you. When this happens several times within a few months you begin to be afraid of what tomorrow might bring to you.

You wonder if your end is near. Your smallest pain, discomfort or digestive disturbance assumes undue importance and, in your mind's eye, presages tragic and fatal consequences. You run to your doctor and when he does not show the same alarm or concern about your condition you hasten to change doctors. You begin to anticipate alarming symptoms and start to compare yours with those of other people. You begin to follow fads, cults, strange cures, and when they fail to satisfy you turn into a hypochondriac.

To avoid these emotional disturbances and to allay your fears of death, keep these salient facts in mind:

1st—You cannot prolong your own life or the life of any other person even for a single moment. It is true that your life span and the expectation to live for others around you is greater today than ever before. But, no one can pinpoint the exact moment of the end for anyone. It is in the hands of God.

2nd—You have no way of telling why someone died at a given time. His death may have been due to some reason unknown to you such as his medical history, a congenital tendency, a predilection to certain diseases, a weakened body condition, a functional or organic disorder, overwork or extreme fatigue, willful bodily or mental abuse, harmful habits or a combination of weakening conditions which began sometime back and finally took their toll. You, on the other hand, may never succumb to such sickness, ailment or circumstance.

3rd—Your chances to recuperate from a serious operation or a prolonged sickness are greater today than ever. With the discovery and the wide use of wonder drugs, with the tremendous advances in surgical practices, and with modern operative and postoperative techniques made available to all patients, everything is in your favor.

Men and women in their seventies and in their eighties undergo surgery undreamed of for them only a few years ago and they fully recover from the disabling and debilitating effects. And now, with the uses of radioactive isotopes, through pinpointed beams and injections so as to eliminate the use of the knife in delicate surgery, new hopes are held out for those afflicated with malignant tumorous growths.

4th—It is not within your power or the power of any man to grant life to someone else. No matter how dear such person might be to you, no matter how much money you have to spend, no matter how many doctors and specialists you engage, there are times when human intervention is of no avail. Worrying about the inevitability of death or grieving continually about someone who was taken from you can do you great physical and emotional harm.

Death is the natural culmination of birth, growth and maturity and there is nothing mortal man can do to change it. So, if you suffered a loss recently or some time ago, learn to accept it as the natural end to all life and carry on in the best way you can. The surest way to help yourself and to assuage the inner inconsolable grief is to continue the work, the projects and the interests of the departed one, if that is possible. This is the practical way to carry on and live your life.

## 5. The Fear of Being Poor or Becoming a Burden on Others

There was a time, not so many years ago, when old age was dreaded and old people were treated shamefully by their families and by society. Those who managed to save some money or had a retirement plan as enforced by the railroads or civil service managed to get along. The rest had to depend upon the will and the whim of their children, take the crumbs and the indignities from their relatives, or were thrown upon local welfare agencies to be shunted from one home for the aged to another.

But times have changed. Now there are Social Security benefits, employee pensions plans, retirement incomes sponsored by unions and trade associations, old-age assistance grants and homes maintained by churches, by fraternal orders and by organizations to take better care of the aged. There are also senior adult groups, civic-minded bodies, county and state Commissions on Aging which are continually at work to improve the lot of the old. Thus, few person past 65 are completely destitute, are a staggering burden upon their families or are left to die, unattended.

Of course, there are many older people who are totally disabled or chronically ill, who are bedridden or senile. They tax the resources of their families and burden the social welfare rolls. That is most unfortunate and there is little you can do about it. By the same token, there are thousands of men and women of young age, and even children, who are incurables, who fill the wards of hospitals and mental institutions, and are a constant drain upon their communities. But such is life and you can do little about changing existing conditions.

If you are poor, let the organizations established for that purpose help you. If you feel you are a burden upon others and you cannot change the conditions which brought it about, make the best of the situation and do all you can to ease things for yourself and those around you. But to worry and to nourish fears will do more harm than good.

## 6. The Fear of Sensory Impairments

Many an older person is highly sensitive about the fact that he has to wear glasses or needs a hearing aid or has to use dentures. His sensitivity may often be only a form of vanity or an assumed self-importance. Then it may also be the refusal to accept older age. But such an attitude cannot change the facts. Sense impairment is a natural sequence of the aging process and no amount of pretense or make-believe can stay the hand of time.

If your eyes have grown weaker, do not refuse to use glasses so as to strengthen your vision. Glasses are not a sign of old age. Look around the next time you are in the midst of people. Note how many men, women and even children wear glasses. They are not sensitive about it and there is no reason why YOU should be.

As to hearing aids, it may surprise you to learn that more people under sixty use hearing aids than those past 65. Literally millions of hearing devices are sold year after year. Many of them are so small and inobtrusive, so cunningly made and used as to defy detection.

As to dentures, do not take it for granted that only older people wear false teeth. Many a glamour star of stage and screen and literally thousands of youngsters wear caps, braces, partials and full bridges of artificial teeth. This is done not only for beauty's sake but for the elementary reasons of being able to bite and to chew.

## 7. The Fear of Old Age

This fear is based upon a misconception. One of the best ways to meet it is to ask yourself—too old for what?

As an older person you may be too old to compete in a sport event where youthful vigor, fleetness of foot or muscular agility is the deciding factor. You may be too old to begin to learn a new trade for a full-time occupation. You may be too old to start a new family and assume the responsibility of raising a new generation of children.

But you can never be too old to be helpful where your training, background and experiences can be used on some mutually agreeable basis. You can never be too old to learn something new to bring you joy, relaxation or satisfaction. You can never be too old to widen your interests, to make new friends, to teach others the things you know well, to engage in activities suitable to your age, to be a friend to others and even to fall in love.

Your children or those twenty or thirty years your junior may call you "old-timer." They may ignore your knowledge or mature judgment and feel that you cannot possibly be "in step" with them and understand them. But do not take such things to heart. Youth is often wasted on the young and many younger people have little patience or tolerance for age. They are so anxious to run things their own way, so confident of their ability to meet their problems, so eager to prove their "coming of age." But when the "going gets tough" they are quick to run to the older folks for help.

## 8. The Fear of Being Looked Upon as a Useless Person

This fear is based upon two misconceptions. First, the enforced retirement from one's regular job and being "sent out to pasture," as it were. Second, the difficulty in finding a new job in commerce and industry due to union rules and Social Security limitations.

Many of those who had to quit their jobs because they reached age 65 have taken their dismissals as a personal affront, as proof that they are no longer needed or wanted, that their usefulness is over. But this is not so. Retirement under the rules of our modern industrial system is not a measure of impaired abilities, declining health, failure in judgment, capacity to continue working, or the indication of the end to one's productivity.

Since World War II, when men and women past 65 were put to work because hands or knowledge or experience were needed, those older employees have proved their worth and dependability over and over again. Many of them stayed on long after the emergency need for additional hands was over. Today there are hundreds of workers in their sixties, seventies and even eighties who hold positions of trust and importance, not only in the business world but also in civic and government posts, to the credit and benefit of all concerned.

The average employer may prefer to have a younger person on a given job in preference to someone advanced in age. This is as it should be. You should never attempt to compete in the open market for the same job which someone twenty or thirty years younger than you can handle better. You have to look for a job where age, experience, knowledge, acquired skills and maturity of judgment count most. Or, if you have no particular skills and training, you have to look for a job where your age in itself, your seeming dependability or your willingness to work for a reduced wage will count.

## 9. THE FEAR OF HAVING NOTHING TO DO

Your fear of having nothing to do may be based upon the experiences of those who never learned what to do with their spare time and are therefore burdened with idle minds and idle hands. If you did not prepare yourself for it before reaching your retirement, it is not too late to begin now. You have the edge on youth insofar as time and opportunity are concerned. The young have jobs to fill, families to feed, obligations to meet, goals to reach, older age to think about and to make provisions for it.

You, on the other hand, are free from those cares and responsibilities. You can follow any wish within the limitations of your age and financial ability. You can follow your natural bent or take up something entirely new and totally different. Your battles are already won. You have no distant future to plan for, to work for, or to dream about. Your future is here, now, and what you do today will determine what you will have tomorrow. So make time count in your favor and start now.

Begin with the work or the occupation you followed before retiring. Was there something in the product, the service, the method of manufacture or in the handling that you would have changed if given the chance? Did you ever want to modify or simplify any phase of that work but were never allowed to do it while working for others? If so, why not try your hand at it now?

Perhaps you can do it at home, on a small scale, without investing too much in materials or equipment. Perhaps you would do better to approach some small, young, ambitious firm in that field and let them provide the necessary tools, materials and equipment. It is conceivable that your idea or your plan would affect desirable savings and prove profitable for you and for those concerned.

## 10. THE FEAR OF BEING UNABLE TO ADJUST YOURSELF

The fear that you may not be able to adapt yourself to new conditions and to changes in your relations and contacts with others stems from the changes in your own daily routines. You followed certain customary procedures through the years, in your working habits and in leisure time activities, and you accepted them as your way of life. Then came the sudden break in the old entrenched habits and if you had not prepared yourself for the changes before your retirement, time hangs heavy on your hands. You have to readjust yourself socially, mentally and emotionally, to your new status and that takes time.

How do you go about it? First, begin to cultivate an open mind and learn to be flexible. Be willing to listen without prejudice or preconceived opinion. Be willing to make allowances for changes or innovations and be ready to try them. Second, accept those changes without fighting them or by trying to maintain the old standards and the old ways.

Those younger than you may have good ideas and they can conceivably be better than your own. The young are not bound by habits and traditions, by set standards and procedures. They can blaze a new trail and quite often come up with newer, better, simpler and more desirable ways to do the old familiar things.

There is a continual change all around you. New products, new methods, new contacts are being developed and discovered nearly every day. Go back in your memory even as little as ten years and compare the changes that took place during that time, and since that time. Think of the new appliances in common use at home and at work and how quickly you have learned to take them for granted. Think of the changes in national and international contacts, the new nations that emerged and the new alliances effected. So—try to be in step with the times and adapt yourself to life around you. Nothing stands still and you are no exception.

Your relations with members of your family and with your children have also undergone changes. If you live with a child, you are the one who has to learn how to adapt yourself to your son-in-law or to your daughter-in-law and to your grandchildren. You are the one who may have to give ground and learn how to remain silent when the urge is strong to "speak your mind" and to meddle in the life of the family.

If you live apart from your children and come to see them at various times you have to exercise the same tolerance, the same impartial approach, the same understanding, and meddle as little as possible in their personal lives. Very few children welcome unasked-for parental advice and interference, especially when they have children of their own and want to handle matters their own way.

But if you feel you have to offer advice and suggest ways to handle a given problem, do it with tact and with a definite "I-leave-it-to-you" attitude. This will save you needless heartaches, prevent misunderstandings, foster a more amiable relationship with the son-in-law or with the daughter-in-law, and tend to make you the welcomed guest whenever you come to visit your children.

Your relations with others, outside of your children, also have to be adjusted. Avoid getting into the habit of complaining about your aches and pains or berating people for their failure to give you their undivided attention or cater to you because you have the weight of your years behind you. Let the things you do and say reflect your change in attitude. That, in turn, will earn for you the respect and the confidence of those with whom you come in contact.

Fears linger where room is left for them to linger. Give them room to grow and they will stay with you. Dissipate them as soon as you can. Go about it deliberately, consistently, and they will not remain to plague you. Look for ways to keep busy in doing things you like to do and you will add to the joys and the meaning of everyday living in your golden age.

# CHAPTER FOUR

# How to Become Lovable at Your Age

Every man wants to be handsome in a manly way and every woman dreams of being beautiful, enticing, desirable, and will go to any lengths to achieve the superficial attributes of physical beauty. But there is no direct connection between beauty of face and form and happy male-female relationships. Great physical beauty inhibits true love because too many, outside of the marriage circle, pay homage to such beauty.

Literally millions of dollars are spent daily by women of all ages and in all walks of life on cosmetics, hair preparations, coiffures, clothing, foundation garments, figure shaping, plastic surgery and other artifices to attain the so-called essential characteristics of physical beauty. But beauty based entirely on make-up, hair-dos, face lifts, girdled figures, plunging necklines and other physical aids cannot foster a lasting love, engender permanent desirable relationships and imbue respect, regard and true admiration. There have to be inner attributes to maintain and retain true love.

Beauty linked only with the overt signs of youth is highly overemphasized and as such does not hold true with facts and with reality. Youth is not always appealing or becoming.

There are literally thousands of young women who are plain and homely and there are women in their sixties and seventies, who in spite of their age, are truly charming and beautiful.

The mistaken belief that youth and beauty are interchangeable and go hand in hand is due mainly to highly publicized beauty contests, to "cheesecake" modeling, to fiction writers, to the movie portrayals of love situations and to the prevailing advertising methods. They stress youthfulness in face and contours as the most essential prerequisite to beauty in woman's eternal search for affection and adoration.

All of this tends to place youth on a pedestal, high above any other age, to be honored, admired, emulated and even worshipped. It encourages the older woman to ape youth and to use every possible artifice to belie her age. These efforts to simulate youth in appearance and in behavior place terrific strains upon the older woman. She takes up strenuous activities, goes on health-injuring reducing diets, forces herself to follow damaging socializing habits and pretends an exuberance which she cannot possibly maintain for any length of time. All of this tends to interfere with her normal physical well-being, upsets her nervous system and affects her emotional stability.

The constant effort to look younger, to act younger, to retain a slim figure and to display shapely curves grows more and more difficult as years are added to one's age. The frantic struggle to "stay the hand of time" engenders growing tensions and emotional blocks which turn eventually into mental ailments.

These older women forget to remember that beauty has its gradations. There is beauty in childhood, in adolescence, in adulthood, in middle age and in the older years. Youth may have verve and vitality, older age has repose and serenity. Youth has its vivaciousness and exuberance, older age its constancy and maturity of judgment.

Of course youth has its tremendous sensory impact with its forms, its seeming newness, its contours and natural loveliness. Youth also has its freshness, its eagerness, its urge to explore and to experiment, its constant drive toward the new and the untried. These are the basic elements of growing up and have to be left behind as the process of growing and maturing is continued.

Love built around youthful features, shapely contours or continual exuberant youth cannot last too long, because physical beauty is transitory and no one can possibly "hold the line" on time. The passing years bring physical changes which no amount of artifices, pretense, coyness, subterfuge or make-believe can fully hide. You may disguise some of the tell-tale marks of time for a while but others will continue to tell the story in many ways.

So—if you passed the fifty-year mark, stop fighting your age. Stop pretending that you are still in the late twenties or early thirties and still have the pep, the energy, the stamina and the vitality of that age. You are fooling no one, least of all those whom you are trying to impress. It tends only to make you look foolish in their eyes. Keep as young as you can in your behavior and in your appearance but let it be in keeping with your age.

This advice for women applies to men as well. Some of them, past their fifties, ape women in the effort to fool others. They use toupees or dye their hair. They undergo face lifts, wear abdominal supports, engage in youthful escapades, copy the younger men in dress and exuberant behavior, assume the roles of gay men-about-town and often take ridiculous chances to impress others with their seemingly inexhaustible reserves of vigor and vitality.

This does not imply that an older man or woman should "let go" and not try to stay presentable and make his best points count. By all means, do the most you can to improve your appearance. Keep up a normal "repair" and "renovating" service, but do not try to "alter" all the signs of your older age. Use modern artifices to compliment you, but do it in moderation. Let those aids give you the assurance you need that you are still "in the running." Let them help you "stay in trim," but remember your age and do not go overboard.

Do not copy the daring styles in dress, in manner and in behavior, of those twenty or thirty years younger than you, and make believe that your older age means nothing at all. Do not feel or pretend that no one will notice the difference or be cognizant of the incongruity. If you are a man, do not flaunt your seeming manly vigor and get into deep waters. If you are a woman, do not make believe you are a "young chick" or assume the pose of a "femme fatale," just because you had a face lift or because your foundation garments or your coy behavior seemingly belie your age. Do not make the mistake of underestimating the intelligence of those who can tell.

Go about building up your charm and personal appeal by developing the attribute of lovableness. It lasts longer, goes deeper and stays with you through the years, even if you do not have Grecian or Patrician features and could never enter a beauty contest. Be lovable. Lovableness is the ability and the capacity to arouse love, to draw people to you, to be charming, to be worthy of regard and adulation, to make people want to be with you and around you.

Lovableness is not effected by age. It is not measured in facial beauty, in curvaceous forms or in youthful effervescence. It is not dependent upon age, height, weight, clothes, wealth, position or station in life. It can flourish anywhere and everywhere. It is something that you can cultivate and acquire, wherever you may be, regardless of race or color, of economic status or physical appearance. Lovableness comes from within and the more you practice it in your contacts with others the greater its appeal and its value.

Lovableness is a composite of habits, attitudes and modes of behavior. It is not only in what you say but how you say it. It is not only in what you do but how you go about it. It is in the reciprocal feeling you engender in those with whom you associate. It is in the impression you convey to others about your character and reactions to given stimuli. It is in the inner qualities and attributes which you have and which you put to use. It is in your learning how to be warm, kind, thoughtful, amiable, considerate, cheerful, cooperative, pleasant and appreciative.

All of these qualities can be nurtured and acquired and here are fifteen ways of how to go about it:

1—Learn to be pliant and to adapt yourself readily to any group or situation without showing disapproval or disdain and without making others feel that you are better than they are.

2—Learn to subordinate your personal likes and preferences while working with others, especially if you agreed to be part of a team or a committee working together toward a common goal.

3—Learn to give of yourself quickly and readily while with others without asking for special recognition or demanding a reward for services rendered.

4—Learn to like people for themselves and not for what they might do for you. Cultivate a warmth in your manner and show an interest in those who come to you, even if you have to pretend.

5—Learn to be true to yourself in the privacy of your heart and remain loyal to those who trust you or confide in you.

6—Learn to control your temper and hold your emotions in check, even when there are many provocations and valid reasons for you to "speak your mind" and put someone "in his place." It may please you but it will seldom "sit well" with others.

7—Learn to maintain an open mind and show respect for the views and opinions of others, especially if they do not agree with you. Every story has two sides, yours and the other fellow's, and you may be on the wrong side. Furthermore, there may be certain aspects about your "stand" which may be wrong or unbeknown to you and therefore merit consideration. So—take time to hear the other side. You may gain by it and at the same time be admired for your fair-mindedness.

8—Learn to set aside preconceived notions and never jump to conclusions. Try to be in step with the need, the time, the group or the circumstance. The old saying, "When in Rome do as the Romans do," has a sound practical basis, and you would do well to follow it if you want to add to your lovableness.

9—Learn to cultivate a sense of humor and the ability to laugh with others, even at your own expense. There is nothing tragic about making a mistake or appearing in a poor light at one time or another. As a human being you have your failings and your shortcomings. To admit them and to laugh at them shows bigness of heart and fairness of mind. What is more, such action on your part may ease a strained situation, prevent needless conflicts and make people "love" you all the more.

10—Learn to live with the inevitable changes which your advanced age brought to you. Do the best you can under the circumstances without building up futile resentments. It will mean less wear and tear on yourself and on those around you.

11—Learn to remain pleasant and courteous at all times, even in the face of open rudeness and bad manners. Do not fall to the level of the uncouth by arguing with him or by showing your displeasure. Ignore the offender, if possible. If not, retain your smile and your pleasant behavior. It will surely endear you to all others, even to those who have misbehaved.

12—Learn to accept with grace and with equanimity the telltale marks of your advancing age without apologies to anyone and without going overboard in trying to conceal your age. There is great dignity and charm in age. Let your golden years add weight and stature to you as a lovable person.

13—Learn to step back now and then to give someone else the chance to shine and be in the limelight for a while. Give the other fellow a boost whenever you can. Go about these things graciously, even if they are only a courtesy on your part and are not expected of you. Such action on your part will never diminish the brightness of your own light and make you all the more lovable.

14—Learn to be quick to apologize if it is expected of you, even when you feel that you are not at fault. Do it when time is of the essence. Do it even when only a child or someone unimportant is concerned. It will be recognized as goodness of heart and greatness of spirit and add much to your lovableness.

15—Learn to show your appreciation and be quick to express it warmly to those who do something for you, even if you are paying for the service rendered. Do it to encourage those who try and they will try all the more next time. Do it to bring a smile to their lips and a warm feeling toward you. The simple words, "Please," or "Thank you," or "How nice of you to do it," are magic phrases that will make people want to do things for you, anytime, all the time.

The fifteen steps given are not all-inclusive, but they can be of great help to you in developing a lovable personality. Cultivate them assiduously by day and by night, wherever you may be, and before long you will have a winning, charming lovableness that will draw people to you. Acquire these various attributes and as surely as the day follows the night you will add much to your joys and happiness in your golden age.

# CHAPTER FIVE

# What is Your Attitude Toward Yourself?

Perhaps at no other time in your life has your mental attitude toward yourself been so important and so far-reaching in its effects upon you as it is now. This is especially true if you are no longer regularly employed and have too much leisure time on your hands.

This is the period in your life when your various sense organs and bodily functions begin to show the signs of age, when minor disorders or degenerative older-age diseases make their initial appearance and bring with them growing ailments and discomforts.

There are justifiable reasons for those disruptive developments in the process of aging. It began with the day of your birth and has continued ever since. Your various senses, organs, glands and the numerous self-operating, self-generating mechanisms in your body have been on the job every moment of your life. They are now showing signs of wear and tear, of abuse and misuse. They are no longer so alert and punctual, so regular and dependable, so active and responsive as they were. They are quicker to resent abuse or mistreatment and show it in the only way they can, in poorer service.

Consider for a moment the responsibilities which your

heart has had to face through the years. It is one of the most amazing, important, delicate and yet most durable organs in your body. It does one third of all the muscular work, yet it weighs only about fifty ounces and in size is not much larger than your fist.

Take time out, right now, for a minute or two, to listen to your heart. If possible, borrow a stethoscope somewhere and as you listen try to impress upon the tablets of your memory that constant life-giving, life-maintaining beat. Try to remember that "dopp-topp," "dopp-topp," as your heart continues the same steady, rhythmic beat, by day and by night, while you work or play, while you are asleep or awake, at the normal rate of seventy-two times a minute. This is more than one hundred thousand times a day or almost forty million times a year. Multiply these figures by number of days and years of your present age and the astronomical number of individual heartbeats should fully impress you.

As a pumping system, your heart circulates the five to six quarts of blood in your body nearly two thousand times a day, an average of ten thousand quarts every twenty-four hours or almost four million quarts of blood each year of your life. Multiply this by the calendar years of your age and let the total number of quarts circulated within you during that time duly impress you.

Your heart, divided into two parts, maintains two separate pumping stations and keeps your blood circulating in two main circuits. The systemic circuit, which starts from the left chamber of your heart, sends the blood through all the arteries, arterioles and capillaries to every cell in your body. In so doing your blood travels a distance of hundreds of miles, from sixty thousand to one hundred thousand miles, during every day of your life.

The pulmonary circuit goes from the right chamber of your heart to the lungs. There it takes up the purified and reoxygenated blood, freed from the waste matter and the carbon dioxide picked up on the return trip through your body, and draws it into the left auricle. From there the blood is emptied into the ventricle below and is started once again on its life-bringing thousand-mile journey through your system.

All of this heart action, known as "systolic" and "diastolic" is electromuscular in nature. The "systolic" is the rhythmic contraction of the ventricles, the "diastolic" is the steady ever-repeating dilatation of the heart. Thus, working in unison, they maintain the familiar "dopp-topp, dopp-topp" beat of your heart that remains almost as constant and neverchanging as time itself.

What a gargantuan task nature entrusted to your heart and how well your heart handles the job even when it is so often abused and mistreated! You, too, may be guilty of it. You, too, may be allowing anger, fear, worry, excitement, strain and overweight to burden your heart needlessly, foolishly.

You may be working too hard under tension or worrying too much. You may be harboring groundless fears or nurturing petty grievances. You may be losing your temper too often, indulging in strenuous sports, following harmful habits or are too tense most of the time, Or, perhaps you lug around too much weight and thus place extra needless burdens upon your heart.

Do you know what it means to be twenty or thirty pounds overweight? Do you know how much harder your heart has to work to send your blood through thousands of extra miles each day and to feed millions of additional cells? Would you like to know what an extra weight is like? Here is a simple way to find out.

Fill a knapsack or a canvas bag with sand or gravel equal to the extra weight your carry over and above your normal weight as determined by your age, sex, height and build. Strap that bag to your shoulders and keep it there for the next twenty-four hours. Wear it while you eat, work, walk, talk, rest, sleep or play. You may not mind the load at first but before long it will start to bother you. Each move you make, each step you take, will begin to tell. The load will grow heavier and heavier, make you all the more conscious of its clumsy heaviness and shut out all thought and usual preoccupation with what you are doing. You will reach the breaking point long before the day is over, perhaps even within a single hour, when you will hasten to remove the pack from your back with a sigh of relief.

That simple experiment should teach you something. It should impress upon you what an extra load is and how much of an additional burden it places upon your heart. It should also remind you that your heart cannot take off that extra load so easily as you did it, by the simple process of removing the pack from your back. It should also remind you that your heart has had to contend with the extra weight ever since you put it on. What is more, you may be adding more poundage right now.

The functions of your heart and the needless burdens you may be placing upon it was taken as only one example of abuse and mistreatment. This may apply to some of your other senses and organs which you have been punishing needlessly, knowingly or not, through the years. You may be doing it because of habit, of carelessness, of self-indulgence or indifference, or because of total disregard for sensible living in keeping with your age and your medical history. You may be shortening your life by eating too much or drinking too much, by keeping late hours or following bad habits and, figuratively speaking, may be digging your own grave.

Good health is dependent upon physical well-being, upon the observance of sensible precautions, upon the avoidance of needless strains and exertions. But it is also greatly affected by your mental attitude, by what you say, by what you do, by the moods you maintain, by the thoughts you entertain and by the way you accept or reject people and conditions around you.

Your mental attitude can instigate all the physical symptoms of a given sickness with all of its attendant pains and discomforts. Yet the most thorough diagnosis may fail to uncover any organic or functional disorder to account for the sickness. Such illness is psychosomatic in origin. That is where medicine is of little help and only psychiatry can get at the basic causes.

Psychosomatic ailments and their impact upon you do not come within the scope of this book. Yet, the suggestions given may help you minimize some of the effects and perhaps eliminate some of the contributing factors.

One of those factors is your attitude toward yourself. It is in how you accept your advancing years and the physical manifestations of your older age. It is in how you maintain and retain your self-respect. It is in your refusal to "give up" and in your resolve not to vegetate. It is in learning how to get along with others in keeping with your status. It is in your readiness to step back willingly, gracefully, and let someone else "carry the ball" in given activities. It is in making the most of what you are and what you can do, within the limitations of your age.

Sociologist David Riesman divides the aged into three groups: the autonomous, the adjustive, and the anomic.

1—Autonomous. The person who ages without much loss in spirit or general activity, who concentrates his interests in narrower fields and sets aside nonessential tiring preoccupations.

2—Adjustive. The person who has been preoccupied with work or position, with prestige or so-called "status," and has to find substitute compensative activities.

3—Anomic. The person who was propped up in the past by his work, interests and various contacts, like so many cards, and when they fell apart with his retirement, he fell with them.

Whatever be the group in which you are to be placed, one thing is certain, you face the same basic problem. If you are not working to supplement your income you have an average of eighty full idle hours each week, and most of them have to be absorbed in some form of interesting and satisfying activity.

It is estimated that one out of every three persons past sixty-five years of age feels displaced in the midst of our modern society. He is not prepared or equipped to fill in his leisure hours, bemoans the loss of old friends and contacts, finds it difficult to make new friends, fights the manifestations of his older age and is reluctant to cultivate new interests and diversions. Behind it all is the general mental attitude that no one needs him or wants him.

There are two schools of thought as to the reasons for the prevalence of such feelings and reactions. One of them, evolved by sociologists Elaine Cummings and William E. Henry as based upon extensive research in Kansas City, is called the theory of "disengagement." As they put it, older age becomes a conscious withdrawal, a steadily decreasing contact with people and things, a growing reluctance to involvements which may call for initiative, exertion or any form of responsibility, and an unconscious preparation for death.

The second theory advanced by gerontologists is that the so-called "disengagement" is mainly a defense mechanism, that basically speaking, individual traits and characteristics do not change with the advance in age, that one who was introvertive or extrovertive in his younger days retains the same tendencies when he grows older. But there is a greater sensitivity toward personal contact and the older person develops the tendency to magnify minor inattentions into deliberate snubs and rejections. These in turn engender unhappiness.

Whether or not you accept either one of these theories as applicable to your own unhappiness, there is one salient fact, it is your attitude toward yourself which minimizes or magnifies the situations or conditions around you. It is your attitude toward yourself and the people and the world around you that adds or takes from your joys and pleasures of everyday living. You have to adjust yourself to your leisure time status. You have to cultivate new concepts of making time your friend and "follow through" on a gradual, consistent and constructive basis.

If, as a man past 65, you are now retired and have no steady job and live in your own home with your wife, keep up some of your old habits. Get up at a reasonable hour every morning, shave, dress neatly, have your breakfast, look through the morning paper and then find something to do outside of the house or in a room where you would not get into your wife's way and interfere with her daily chores.

If your wife is no longer with you and you live with a

child or with strangers, follow the same general routine. Find something to do and some place to go, away from the house. The day you begin staying in bed most of the morning, the day you pass up your customary shave, the day you become satisfied to wear anything so long as it covers your body, the day you become indifferent to your looks and appearance, that will be the beginning of your decline. That will be the day when you start losing your self-respect and "go to seed."

If you are a woman past 65 who has no steady job, who lives alone and has no set duties, follow the same general routine of being presentable at all times. Do not loll about in bed at all hours. Do not fail to make up your face, fix your hair and put on a suitable dress. Walking around in dishabille may be homely but hardly flattering to you. Someone, even if only a neighbor, will see it and think disparagingly of you. What is more, you will start thinking less of yourself and before long lose your self-respect.

If you are a woman living alone, do not get into the habit of cheating on your food intake. Do not be satisfied with the "widow's meal," by grabbing a bite of this, a sip of that, a taste of something else and a few forkfuls of "left-overs" from the day or night before and calling it a meal.

You will fool your digestive system for a while and even lose a pound or two in weight, but your system will not accept it too long. Soon that starvation diet will show up in your lack of energy, in tiredness or listlessness, in nervous tension and growing irritabilities. It will also show up in your contacts with others because it will tend to make you cross, gloomy, sensitive and quarrelsome.

It takes effort and application, desire and constant watchfulness to maintain the proper mental attitude toward yourself. Unfortunately for you, as an older person, your family, your friends and many of the others with whom you come in contact, give you little encouragement. Due to indifference or disinterest, to lack of sympathy or understanding, to misconception and general apathy, those younger than you often undermine your effort to retain the right mental attitude. They refer too often to the "weight of your years" and are forever cautioning you not to do this or that because you are too old.

Added to those constant admonitions to "know your place," to be extra careful, to step aside, to stay on the sidelines, are the natural physical manifestations of your advancing years which tend to upset you. In addition, there are the social and work restrictions placed on you and the mental imbalance they foster because of your personal resentments and your aversion to being considered "old," or "going downhill," as it were.

All of these things tend to bring grim lines to your lips, a dour look to your face and an embittered outlook on life. They cut deeply into you and keep you from having the right mental attitude toward yourself and taking advantage of all the good things life can offer you, today, now.

What are the steps you can take to offset those disturbing influences and properly cultivate the desired mental attitude? Here are a number of them:

1—Begin with a frank personal appraisal. How do you "stack up" against others in your age group, in your circumstances and in your circle of friends and acquaintances? Are you as good or better than they are? Are there any among them who are more popular than the rest, who are the leaders, who have more friends, who stand out from the rest? Can you measure up to one of them? What is your personal opinion of yourself as a parent, a spouse, a neighbor, a co-worker, a friend or a citizen of your community?

Would you employ someone like you in a position calling for initiative, leadership, and the ability to uncover the potentialities of those under you? Would you take someone like you in a business calling for resourcefulness, strength of character and the ability to withstand hardships and setbacks? Would you be willing to entrust all of your worldly goods to someone like you and be guided by his judgments and decisions? And, if you needed a friend, someone who will remain true and loyal to you, would you choose someone like yourself, knowing what you know about your failings and shortcomings?

Put these questions down on paper. Add other similar questions to the list and take time to ponder over them before you answer them. Be honest and straightforward in your replies. Let them be the true account of your feelings. Let them show your true character. Then, and only then, you could use them as guides to help you cultivate the attributes needed so as to acquire the right mental attitude toward yourself and toward others.

2—Accept the various manifestations of your age in the proper spirit and in their realistic perspective. There is nothing shameful or disgraceful about growing older. The feeling of shame lies in the foolish, frantic efforts to hide and to disguise all the marks of time.

It is desirable to be in step with the times. It is advisable to utilize modern aids to minimize some of the glaring effects of time. But it should be done in a sensible manner and not become a race against time. You can never win that way. Cultivate instead a youthful outlook upon things and people around you and let that help you maintain and retain the right mental attitude toward yourself and toward others.

3—Stop fooling yourself by pretending that you are not a day older than you were ten or twenty years ago. Stop fooling yourself by maintaining the old habits and pursuits in the fond hope that no one will notice the difference in you. It is the wrong attitude to take. You are overtaxing your strength, cutting into your reserves and are actually shortening your life.

Cultivate instead those activities which are more in keeping with your age and your capacities. Follow only those diversions and recreations, those habits and modes of living which do not leave unpleasant aftermaths in physical strain, in nervous exhaustion and in mental disquietude.

4—Begin to use this day to its best advantage. Stop regretting the past, bemoaning your older age or bewailing the seeming injustice of your growing impairments or discomforts. Some of them can be minimized but others cannot. Know which is which and live accordingly. Take life in your stride and make the best of every moment.

There are many things you can do and many things you can enjoy if you only open your eyes, your ears, your mind and your heart. It is in the way you go about it, in the mental attitude you maintain that will determine your joys and your pleasures on this day.

5—Begin to accept your status as an older person, with all that it implies. If you still have to work side by side with others younger than you, be willing to "step back," to take "second best," especially where good sight, dexterity of hand or muscular stamina is a requisite. If you are engaging in sports, let the younger fellow do the jumping, the running, the catching, while you serve as judge, umpire, critic or reviewer. If you are a member of a given group, let the younger members take the lead and the burdens of carrying through certain projects, especially where youthful drive and vigor are important, while you concentrate on the administrative or advisory end where judgment, maturity and experience count.

6—Retain a firm control over your financial assets. It is advisable, in many cases, to turn over a business to one's children and to give financial support to those who need help. But do not drain yourself dry. Do not give everything away in the hope that those gifts will assure you loving care and tender devotion for the years to come. Children and friends have notoriously short memories and regrets are a poor substitute for shortsightedness. If you are fortunate enough to have financial independence now, hold on to it. It is one of the surest ways to maintain carefree living and to retain a healthy mental attitude.

7—Utilize one of the greatest assets you have—time. Use it well for your benefit and enjoyment. Take time to go places. Take time to laugh, to dance, to swim, to paint, to read, to make friends, to enjoy all the things that modern life has to offer.

8—Cultivate a cheerful spirit. Develop the facility to see the bright and sunny side of things no matter how dull or drab they happen to be. Look for the good in the people you meet and let your warmth and friendliness come through. This will help you in several ways. It will banish your feeling of boredom and loneliness. It will enable you to maintain a better mental attitude toward yourself. It will draw people to you and bring you the sense of belonging, so important to your physical and mental well-being.

9—To help you generate the proper desirable mental attitude, get into the habit of lolling about for a while each day. Just sit back in a comfortable seat and relax. Let your thoughts drift along idly, lazily, without forcing yourself to grapple with a given problem and without trying to think your way through.

Bask in the warmth of the sun. Watch the clouds scurry by. Surround yourself with the strains of soothing music or the playful preoccupations of a child. Watch birds on the wing or tree leaves sway gently in the breeze. Make conversation with a youngster or a neighbor and let time pass you by. Put moments of idleness in between your various activities without feeling guilty about it and without apologizing to anyone for your seeming laziness. Then you will surely gain a greater measure of satisfaction and enjoyment as time goes by.

10—To maintain the proper mental attitude toward yourself you have to cultivate self-respect and never sell yourself short. The loss of self-respect is the first step toward vegetation and degeneration no matter how good your health might be and how many years are still ahead for you. This holds true for you, as a man or a woman, regardless of your financial status and your position in life.

The loss of self-respect becomes the tendency to "let go." You stop thinking of yourself as a total entity, as someone worthy of trust, confidence and consideration. You sink lower and lower in self-esteem. You begin to look and to act as if nothing mattered any more to you, as if life and all that it holds for you lost its value and meaning to you. You may even develop an anti-social attitude.

For a while you may still perk up a little to please yourself and to meet others. But before long your new mental attitude starts to influence you, and you fall under its disintegrating dominance. You become untidy and begin to neglect common social usages and amenities. You begin to say to yourself—"Oh, what's the use! Nobody cares for me. Nobody wants me . . ."

This shows up in your general behavior and people start to avoid your company. It increases your feeling of insecurity, of inferiority. You start to look for excuses to justify your self-negligence, in poor health, in the lack of interest or attention paid to you. This leads to psychosomatic ailments and before long you are the victim of your own induced and distorted mental attitude.

You must retain your self-respect. It is the determination to do nothing at any time, even in the privacy of your heart, that would tend to lower your estimate of yourself and cheapen you in your own eyes. Self-respect begets self-assurance and fosters self-confidence. They are most important to you at this time, especially when you have the leisure hours to favor yourself, to indulge your whims, to follow your inclinations, and to pay more attention to your ways of thinking.

To paraphrase a passage from the book *How to Conquer Fears, Worries and Frustrations in 30 Hours*, ". . . You must have confidence in your own importance and belief in your own contributions to life around you, however small they might be, or else you have no basis for belief in anything or in anyone. . . . You must have self-assurance and belief in yourself first before others will accept you at your valuation and be willing to place their trust, confidence and respect in you. . . ."

Self-confidence promotes mental balance and emotional stability. It engenders the right mental attitude toward yourself and the world around you. It fosters a healthy regard for the value and the importance of your own views and convictions and at the same time leaves room for a divergence of opinion.

All of this tends to keep you "on an even keel" emotionally. It establishes better and friendlier relationships with those you meet at home, at work, at play, or wherever it might be. It also helps you to be more amenable to changes and to innovations in life around you.

Follow these various steps to acquire the right mental attitude. Adapt them to your make-up and personality. Then, no matter what your sex, age, looks, education, position or financial status, people will seek your company and advice and want to be with you. Then life will become sweeter and brighter for you as you add new joys to your golden age.

# CHAPTER SIX

# Old Age and Your Physical Health

Aging and the gradual debility that follows as a natural sequence in the aging process is something which neither you nor anyone else can ever escape. However, the attendant effects upon your bodily functions and upon your sensory and mental systems can be arrested and minimized.

The degenerative diseases of older age, aside from the impairment of vision, of hearing, and the decline in motor nerve and muscular reaction, come under four general categories: 1) The metabolic. 2) The arthritic. 3) The tumorous. 4) The vascular system disorders.

Those conditions are insidious. They start unknowingly to you and develop gradually and consistently over a long period of time. For instance, in arteriosclerosis there is a gradual rise in blood pressure. In arthritis, there are the consistent, recurring slight aches in the bones and a gradual stiffness in muscles. This stiffness may show up only upon arising in the morning or when you maintain a given position for any length of time.

Many new ways have been found to cope with degenerative diseases in their initial stages and your chances to reach your seventies, eighties and even nineties, in spite of disease, are greater today than ever before in the history of man. Your span of longevity is lengthened year after year as newer, surer and quicker ways are discovered to stop the inroads of sicknesses, to nullify their effect upon you and to add more years to your life.

On the basis of the Commissioner's Mortality Tables, adopted in 1941 by all life insurance companies, the life expectancy of older adults is as follows: for age 65—an additional 11.55 years; for age 70—8.99 years; for age 75—6.82 years, for age 80—5.06 years, with women having a 5.00-year edge over men.

Those mortality tables were compiled in 1940. Since then with the discovery and the widespread use of sulpha drugs which minimize the danger of acute and chronic infectious disease, with penicillin, with antibiotics and antihistamines, and many other wonder drugs in use, coupled with newer operating techniques to combat postoperative complications, your chances to live longer are growing better from day to day.

According to a special survey made in 1959 there were more than twenty-nine thousand men and women in America aged ninety-five and over. Most of them were in good health, mentally alert and seemingly set to carry on for many more years. Since 1959, medical science took many giant steps forward. For instance, if you ever were anesthetized and later had to be taken to a recovery room to wear off some of the effects, if you ever went through the attendant nausea, nervous shock, digestive disturbances and other discomforts of a spinal injection or other form of usual anesthesia, you will be interested in the new ways of anesthetizing.

Nowadays patients can be prepared for operations and be put to sleep in less than a minute via electric currents, and all it takes is the flick of a switch. A frequency generator providing a 700-cycle electric current through an amplifier is connected to the patient's temple with small electrodes. A switch is flicked on and within thirty to sixty seconds the patient falls asleep and remains unconscious as long as the current is on.

This new way of anesthetizing was used for the first time by a team of surgeons in the University of Mississippi Medical Center on a woman patient. Within one minute after the operation she regained full consciousness and was taken to her room. The electric anesthesia left her without nausea or other ill effects and without the discomforts or occasional complications which come at times with the usual postoperative awakening.

Other important strides in surgical techniques have been made since 1959, such as the uses of microscopic sights and needle-like knives in tympanoplastic surgery. This refers to an operation within the human ear, where a perforated eardrum is replaced by a skin graft from the patient's own skin or vein. Or the performance of delicate surgical operations without the use of a knife, and the use of new sutures that actually promote the healing.

For instance, in Sweden some time ago, a delicate brain operation was performed by the use of an atomic beam of protons. It was directed at the head of a patient and focused upon a small malignant growth in the brain. The beam penetrated the flesh and the bone without harm to them. It destroyed the tumorous growth but left the surrounding healthy tissues untouched. Thus, a delicate brain operation was done successfully without opening the skull, without using a scal-

pel and without subjecting the patient to the attendant preoperative and postoperative procedures and possible complications.

The treatment of cancerous growths with radioactive elements, especially with radiated cobalt, is growing steadily.
It speaks well for the victims of this dread disease. Sometimes the pinpointed radioactive beams are combined with
surgery if it is deemed necessary. The beams destroy the
cancer cells and the surgery removes the core of the cancer.
At other times the process is reversed. The surgery comes first
and the radiations are used afterwards to kill stray cancer
cells.

The radioactive cobalt is only one of several ways in
which atomic rays are utilized. Pellets, sutures and tiny ray-
emitting rods are used. For instance, in the cancer of the
breast doses of either radioactivated cobalt, irridium or tel-
lurium, encased in nylon tubes, are placed to attack and to
destroy the cancerous cells which were missed and were not
removed during surgery.

Radioactivated ingredients are also used in solutions in-
jected into the affected areas. Others are put into a liquid
form to be taken orally, such as irradiated iodine to attack
an infected thyroid gland. And hope is now held out for the
sufferers of psoriasis through the external application of radiated lotions.

The field of electronics is also contributing to medical
science to combat hitherto fatal sicknesses. For instance, in
cases of double pneumonia, especially when they are aggravated by toxemia, anemia or a weakened heart, and an iron
lung is too cumbersome to use, doctors can now utilize the
Barnett Ventilator. It is a portable electronic breathing de-
vice which, like the iron lung, will pump specified amounts

of air into the patient's lungs. The ventilator is portable, more flexible in use, provides greater freedom of movement and has been instrumental in saving many additional lives.

The electronic and the atomic age are here. And medical science is making tremendous strides in the uses of electronics and radioactive isotopes to check and to combat serious ailments and the inroads of malignant tumerous conditions.

Now modern research comes up with new theories of the relation between the time elements and the health of man. It is new research in the field of bio-rhythms. The researchers contend that biological clocks within the human organism play an important part in the aging process, and because those internal timepieces slow down or speed up at times, some people age quicker.

It is claimed that the new modes of jet travel and the changes in temperature zones as well as time differences in various global areas have definite and potentially harmful effects upon one's innate biological rhythms. It is a known fact that when someone moves from the East to the West Coast, or from a temperate to a torrid zone, his body temperature, blood cell count, sleep and food routine, as well as the secretions of body hormones continue to synchronize with the temperature and the time standard he left behind. It takes a while for those biological rhythms to adjust themselves to the new zone or the new time standard and such oftentimes affect a given person adversely.

Dr. Curt P. Richter of Johns Hopkins University said: "Human beings harbor many internal clocks, apparently independent of all external influences, temperature, humidity and barometric pressure as well as day-to-day emotional disturbances. Each unit has an individual and inherent cycle, which may operate independently of its neighbors. In a normal, healthy organ these units function out of phases. Some are active, others are at rest. Shock or trauma may synchronize the phases and the result is illness. Conversely, an interference in the tick-tocks of the internal clocks, such as a given drug, may desynchronize the cycles and return the organ to good health."

There is strong evidence of a close connection between the natural rhythms of the human body and health. Thus, the science of bio-rhythms, like biochemistry, may soon utilize its knowledge to help man achieve a longer, healthier life.

Yet in spite of all advances in man's efforts to prolong life, the process of aging brings many physiological and psychological changes. Some of them are inevitable, others may affect someone else and not you. Among them are:

1—A gradual slow-down in blood circulation and a rise in blood pressure. Your vascular system undergoes the aging process and may lead to the hardening of the arteries. This is where your doctor can help you to arrest the rising blood pressure.

2—A gradual change in metabolism. The anabolic processes in your body start to fail in some of their functions. The quantities of important digestive juices secreted by your system is lowered and your ability to digest rich, heavy foods is lessened. You may need food supplements or medications to correct the situation and only your doctor is best equipped to prescribe them for you.

3—Decreasing energy requirements. You need smaller amounts of fats and sugars in your daily food intake. This may restrict your consumption of candies, pastries, gravies, fried dishes and other high-caloried foods.

4—You may have a chewing problem and choose to omit steaks, raw fruits and vegetables from your diet. But this need not be so. You can get better, closer fitting dentures. You can have your butcher grind the favorite cuts of lean meat for you. You can use tenderizers to soften steaks and chops. You can have your raw fruits and vegetables diced or chopped, shredded or liquefied with the aid of a home-type juice blender.

5—A growing impairment in sense impressions. Your eyes and ears may lose some of their sharpness and you may develop a wobbliness in your knees and soreness in your legs. This calls for glasses or a hearing aid or a cane or greater care in crossing the street, climbing stairs and taking lengthy walks.

6—Changes in skin texture and resiliency. Your skin begins to lose its normal elasticity, the sweat secretions are lowered and the amount of subcutaneous fat is thinned out. Various pigmented spots and keratoses appear on your hands, face and other parts of the body. The veins increase in size, show up more prominently and the small blood vessels become more fragile as your skin dehydrates, gets shiny and finely wrinkled. This makes your skin more susceptible to infection, to inflammation and troublesome bleeding even from minor and seemingly small blows.

7—Your ability to fall asleep quickly and sleep soundly through the night is lessened. Of course, as an older person who is no longer steadily employed and expends little muscular energy you do not need a full eight or nine-hour sleep. But if your sleep is fitful, if the slightest noise awakens you and keeps you awake for hours, you need help. Then be sure not to use widely publicized sleeping pills without consulting your doctor. Medical help is part of his training and knowledge and it is not in the province of salesmen and copywriters.

8—Greater preoperative and postoperative risks. The older person faces greater risks when in need of surgery. His doctor has to evaluate not only the physiological and pathological aspects of the proposed surgery or the resulting shock to the physical and nervous systems, but also the renal, adrenal, pulmonary and cardiovascular status of the patient. So—if you are past 65 and need surgery, be sure to check with several doctors.

9—Muscular soreness. There is a greater tendency to increased sensitivity in joints and muscles. You may have frequent backaches, mysterious kinks and sore spots, and find it more difficult to bend, to twist, to walk fast or exert muscular efforts for any length of time. All of this may be the forerunner of an arthritic condition and your doctor can prescribe ways to arrest it and to minimize its effects upon you.

10—There is a gradual slowdown in usual, normal reflex actions. You are no longer so quick to respond to an emergency, so alert in your reactions as you used to be. Hence, any activity requiring quick coordination, an immediate response or sustained undivided attention may become too difficult for you to follow.

11—There is a growing sensitivity to noise, to crowds, to changes in the weather, to children playing nearby, to trivial discomforts or to minor changes in habitual routines. Small things which never bothered you before are quick to annoy you, to upset you. They build up tensions within you and lead to growing irritations and outbursts of temper.

12—There is an increasing tendency to forget details, to let your mind wander and to have occasional lapses of memory. Thus, anything you want to do which entails too many details or calls for an unfailing memory may become a tiresome and exhaustive chore for you.

13—There is a greater inclination to live in the past, to dwell at length upon what was, to regret the passing of time, to yearn passionately for the good old days. In some instances this constant yearning may turn into a regression to one's childhood, to childish actions, feelings, wishes and desires.

14—There is an increasing preoccupation with your bodily functions and a growing worry about them. Thus, a shortness of breath or a quickening of the heartbeat due to anger or anxiety, flatulence or a touch of indigestion because of hurried eating, a minor pain or discomfort or some trivial annoyance evokes a major emotional upset and builds up needless apprehensions.

15—There is an increased suspicion of the motives behind the behavior of members of one's family and the growing belief that they are scheming to "fleece" you. So, you tighten your purse strings or start to dissipate your financial resources or in a "fit" make a new will, cut off the family with a dollar each and "will" your worldly assets to some outlandish beneficiaries.

16—There is a growing feeling that people shun you deliberately or dislike you on general principles. You begin to feel you are an "outsider" in the bosom of your family and an "interloper" wherever you go. You magnify the smallest oversight, the simplest inocuous lack of attention and begin to take them to heart. This engenders a mounting feeling of insecurity and leads to an entrenched inferiority complex.

17—There is a steady warping of good judgment and

common ordinary reactions. You lose your sense of values and moral standards. You go "all out" for some strange fad, cult or induced belief. The sexual urge is magnified and in some cases leads to indecent exposure, to improper advances toward members of the opposite sex, in private and in public. It also leads to ridiculous January-July misalliances which bring in their wake shame, ruin, heartache, dishonor and costly litigation as an aftermath of the eventual crude awakening.

18—There is often a flat refusal to accept one's older age, and a round of frantic, futile attempts to "stay the hand of time." These lead to costly face lifts, to bizzare make-ups, to excesses in sport activities, to injudicious night life, to the uses of estrogen or testosterone propionates, to sex hormone preparations, or to the nerve-tensing play-acting at being a "play girl," a "merry widow," a "gay blade" or a veritable Casanova.

19—There is a tendency to use one's old age as the excuse for self-pity, for laziness, or for the unwillingness to tend to one's personal needs. The older age becomes the "club" to enforce care and attention. This gives the older person a sense of security and importance, but it makes him a troublesome, bothersome person and quickly antagonizes members of his family and others around him.

20—There is a complete capitulation to old age and the abandonment of all desire to be self-sufficient and make the most of what one can do for himself. The oldster begins to feel and to act as if every day is his last day on earth. So, he "gives up." He lets go. He vegetates. And when some minor sickness overtakes him he goes to bed and remains there, safe in the knowledge that someone will take care of him until the end comes.

If any of these changes and tendencies apply to you, take steps to avoid them and minimize them as quickly as you can. Refuse to "grow old disgracefully." Benefit by the knowledge, wisdom and maturity you accumulated through the years. Capitalize upon the experience you gained. And here are a few suggestions based upon the findings and the recommendations of geriatricians and psychiatrists.

## Preserve Your Health

A. Through Preventive Geriatrics. Let your doctor identify the danger signs and prescribe ways to arrest and to prevent the initial inroads of degenerative diseases. Part of the cure may be in restricting old habits, in recommending certain foods and in the use of various pills and medications to offset the development of disabling ailments and conditions.

B. Through Palliative Geriatrics. Let your doctor institute treatments and prescribe medications to ease the pains and the discomforts of such ailments which can no longer be prevented or eliminated.

C. Through Constructive Geriatrics. Let your doctor teach you how to live with existing conditions and get more ease and comfort within the limitations already in effect.

## Watch Your Diet

Even if there is no need for it, let your doctor list for you the foods you should and should not eat. You may be eating too much of rich, highly seasoned dishes, heavy with condiments and animal fats. You may be having too much of gravies, pastries, hard liquors and sweetened drinks. You could work off the extra calories before but not anymore, and are adding unnecessary girth to your hips or midriff.

Perhaps you have been using reducing pills or liquids to cut down your weight but are not successful at it. A better and simpler way would be to cut down the food intake. Begin doing it by using a smaller plate and putting less food on it. Cut down on gravies, second helpings and rich pies or deserts. Take smaller bites and eat slower. Stop eating between meals, munching sweets or nuts or raiding the refrigerator at odd hours.

Cut down on starches and carbohydrates. Go easier on condiments and limit your consumption of sweet drinks, sundaes and malts. Eat more raw fruits and vegetables, more lean meat and fish and less of delicatessen specialties. Go heavier on milk and easier on coffee, especially at night.

Your doctor may urge you to masticate your food more thoroughly and drink more water during the day. To paraphrase a passage from *How to Conquer Fears, Worries and Frustrations in 30 Hours*, ". . . Take more time to eat, not so much to consume more food but to eat less hurriedly. Give the ptyalin in your saliva the time it needs to convert starch into dextrose before you send the food into your stomach. Your twenty-six feet of twisted, coiled intestines have enough work to do without being forced to accept dry, hard, half-chewed chunks of miscellaneous food. Masticate every bite. Let it be dexterized and pepsinized properly and you will hardly ever have digestive troubles . . ."

B. Your elimination process may not be regular at this time and you may need an occasional nudge, but whatever else you do, stay away from highly advertised laxatives, purgatives and so-called natural preparations. Let your doctor prescribe the proper help. One of the simplest ways to maintain regular elimination is to establish a pattern, to set a given time for it, preferably upon arising, and encourage it by trying again and again, day after day, at the same time. Before long you will form the habit and be set.

One doctor recommends this method: "As you take the seat in the bathroom, begin to inhale and exhale slowly, deeply, regularly, several times. Then hold your breath as long as you can and let go of all tension. Imagine for a moment that your head is under water and it must remain submerged as long as it is humanly possible. This prolonged breath control tends to expand the intestinal tract, intensifies peristaltic action and induces a natural bowel movement. You may have to hold your breath several times in a row at first until your tenseness is gone and you relax completely." This idea worked well for others and may be helpful to you.

### Get Adequate Rest, Exercise and Relaxation

Take a nap every day. The duration is not so important as the fact that you are resting and relaxing. One way to encourage the facility to drop off to sleep for a while during the day is to set aside a definite time for it, every day. Make sure to shut out as much light and noise as you can from the room, stretch out on a bed or a couch, close your eyes, begin to breathe slowly, deeply, and "let go" of all tenseness in your muscles. Do it for several days in a row and continue doing it until the habit is formed and comes to your aid.

B. Learn to relax often during the day and evening, even if it is only for two or three minutes at a time. The knack is not in making the effort but in learning how to grow limp and loose. For instance, when sitting down do not perch on the edge of the chair as if poised for a sudden flight, but sit all the way back. If the chair has a back, let your spine be in a straight line. If it is an easy chair, adopt a position that is comfortable and relaxing for you. If you are working at something, go about it in a calm, orderly fashion rather than in spurts and splurges. In other words, do not waste nervous energy. Take things easy and cultivate poise and composure in whatever you do.

C. Exercise moderately every day. Do it regularly and let it be in keeping with your age and your limitations. Take up swimming, dancing, golf, hiking, flower cultivation or anything else that calls for some form of muscular activity and physical application. Pills, vitamins and medications may provide you with missing nutrients but they cannot become the substitute for the exercise you need to promote healthy living.

Exercise assumes greater importance to you as you grow older and as your various organs and muscles lose some of their former resiliency and elasticity. Even your blood vessels, which are lined with smooth muscle tissue, need to be expanded and contracted from time to time so as not to become flabby. You can do this only through various exercises and activities which force more blood through your system.

Calisthenics, on a regular basis, followed day after day, will do wonders for you. It will "firm" your muscles, "tone" your system, "condition" your body, improve your digestion, promote regularity, and like a tonic, help you to ward off sickness.

However, heed this note of warning. Do not go in for strenuous exercises, especially if you are not used to them. Be sure to check things with your doctor to be certain that you are not overtaxing your strength or sapping your energies. Watch the aftereffects and if you are too tired or cannot catch your breath or show other signs of exhaustion, watch out.

Moderation in everything you do, in eating or sleeping,

in working or playing, in reading or watching TV, in doing exercises or in following any activity, is the keynote to healthier living. To grow with your years and to enjoy all the days of your life is a matter of sane, sensible behavior in keeping with your age and its attendant limitations. When you become too greedy for life, when you begin to burn the candle at both ends so as to make up for lost time, you lose peace and tranquility.

It is wonderful to have a cause to work for, a goal to aim at, a mission to meet and to fulfill. You are never too old to take up a worth-while project. But never allow yourself to "go overboard" and become a zealot or a fanatic, no matter how imbued you might be with the basic aims of your project.

Leave room for other interests and diversions. Leave room for a difference and a divergence of opinion. Take your time in whatever you do. Let it be a joyous, relaxing task and not a chore. Even if you are trying to learn something, do not cram your studies and do not try to beat time. You have no future to plan for and no new worlds to conquer.

What is more, be true to yourself. Take pride in the things you do and can do. Do them as well as you can and they will bring you a sense of accomplishment. Cultivate at the same time a goodness of heart and a warm friendly feeling to all with whom you come in contact. Then you will surely find the gold in your golden age.

# CHAPTER SEVEN

# How to Live With an Infirmity

How do you live with an impairment which cannot be changed? How do you adapt yourself to conditions beyond your control? Perhaps this incident will be illuminating.

An old man was walking slowly, painfully along the sidewalk, lifting each foot with evident effort and leaning heavily on a sturdy cane. He reached the corner, waited for the light to change and, stepping cautiously off the curb, began to navigate the busy thoroughfare with faltering steps.

A young, comely woman, nicely dressed, coming swiftly behind him slowed down and offered her arm to help him across. He smiled, declined the offer and said: "Thank you, my dear. I'm in no hurry to reach the other side. The traffic will wait. It always does. But I wouldn't mind having you beside me, that is, if you can spare the extra minute or two. . . ."

He gave her another smile and continued: "There was many a time, not so long ago, when I, too, was always in a hurry. I chased time all the time but somehow I could never catch up with it. Meanwhile, I had no time for myself, for my family and for the many things I would have liked to do.

98

Then when my retirement came I was all set to go places and do things. But an automobile accident affected my legs and it looked as if I'd have to spend the rest of my life in a wheel chair.

"I refused to stay put and insisted on trying to walk. It was so hard, so painful. Each step was a new source of agony, but I refused to give up, and as you see I manage to get by. Of course, I can't run or walk as steadily as others. It bothered me at first but I don't let it depress me in any way now. As a matter of fact, my slow walk and this cane of mine have been a sort of blessing these last two years. . . ."

He emphasized the last few words with several thumps of his cane. The woman gave him a puzzled look. He ignored it and went on: "Yes, my cane has been a blessing. Wherever I go people are always ready and eager to help me. Take you, for instance, would you have taken the time to stop and to offer me your arm if I were hale and hearty and did not need a cane? . . ."

She started to protest. He silenced her with a chuckle and continued: "That's so, and we both know it. But aside from being a source of contact with other people my cane has helped me in other ways. It slowed me down a great deal. It takes me longer to go from place to place. That gives me much more time to pause, to look and to see, to hear and to listen, to notice and observe, to enjoy and to appreciate many things which I missed before, because now time is on my side. . . .

"Tell me, my dear, and you're such a pretty thing I must say, have you ever seen a mother bird teach a fledgling how to fly? Have you ever watched a flower open its petals to the sun or sway gently to the tunes of a breeze? Have you ever seen a kitten play with a ball, a twig or a piece of string and make believe the plaything was alive? Have you ever heard a little girl coo and lull her doll to sleep with a wordless lullaby? Have you ever watched shadows dance on a wall? Have you ever seen butterflies chase each other in soaring, swooping, swirling spurts of flight?

"Have you ever sat near an open window in the still of the night, watched fleecy clouds drift by, caught a shooting star on the wing, and in the midst of it let a sense of peace and wonder pass over you? Have you ever listened with your heart to the joyous laughter of a child bubbling over something utterly silly to you? Have you ever watched a dog tease its master to play the game of "come-and-catch-me"? Have you ever felt the lovelight of someone's glance caress you clear across a room? And, have you ever heard a silly old man chatter away as I have been doing? . . ." He chuckled and added quickly: "But perhaps I'm not so silly after all, because here I've been keeping you at my side for some time . . . Isn't it so?"

The two crossed the busy intersection. The old man with the cane turned to the left, waving "good-bye" to his companion. She waved back and let a smile play on her lips. It lingered on as she slowed down unconsciously for a while before she resumed her brisk walk.

Does this incident tell a story? You be the judge of it. One thing is certain, your attitude has a great deal to do with the way you accept and live with a condition beyond your control. So—when you begin to feel sorry for yourself because you are growing older or because you have an impairment, take time out to look around. Take time to see a blind person carrying on in spite of his terrific handicap. Take time to visit a school for the deaf-mutes or a rehabilitation center for disabled war veterans or a mental institution. And later, in the privacy of your room, begin to compare your lot with those you saw. It is bound to do you a world of good and provide you with the impetus and the courage you need to carry on.

Many a handicap has been turned into an asset. Perhaps this paraphrased poem by Schiller may give you food for thought:

"When God created the birds of the world he gave many of them colorful plumage, sweet voices and cheery hearts but no wings. He placed wing-like appendages upon the ground near each bird and said, "These shall be your joys or your sorrows, your helpmates or handicaps. Carry them with you at all times . . ." The birds did not question God. They lifted the appendages, held them close to their little hearts, and hopping clumsily from place to place continued to sing cheerfully and joyfully. Soon the appendages grew fast to their sides and became pinions fair to carry the birds high into the air . . ."

If you envy others who seemingly have more than you, if you covet their wealth or health and the other things which they have, you may be in gross error, because you have no way of telling what troubles they have, and how better off you may happen to be.

Everyone of us has a cross to bear. It is in the very nature of life. We all have cares and burdens, worries and responsibilities, sorrows and ailments, infirmities or inner troubles, broken dreams and disappointments. Thus, whether we are young or old, rich or poor, we have a cross to carry. If we do it with simplicity, equanimity and forbearance, without adding to it the weight of greed, envy, jealousy, selfishness and intolerance, we lighten our cross and find it easier to carry.

To paraphrase Aughey: "God in His heavens makes many crosses, of different weights and sizes. Some are of iron and lead. They look as if they might crush the bearer but they never do. Others are made of straw. They seem light but they cling close and are no less difficult to carry. Still others are made of gold and precious stones. They dazzle the eye and excite envy in others, but only those who are saddled with such crosses know their enormous weight."

A story is told of a holy man, hailed as a miracle worker, who was on a pilgrimage and stopped overnight in a small inland town never before visited by him. It was a fairly prosperous place but its people were not happy. Greed, envy and jealousy were rampant there. The moment the townspeople learned the holy man was among them they hastened to besiege him. Each was asking for something. Each wanted his neighbor's home, cattle, money and other possessions.

The holy man dwelt upon the fallacy of envy but none would heed his words. The clamor for his miracles grew more and more insistent and none would leave until he would agree to do something. He finally selected four persons from those who clamored most for his intervention and handed each a sheet of paper and an envelope. He asked each to list in detail his troubles, his sorrows and the things he wanted most. The lists were to be inserted in the blank envelopes, sealed and handed back to him. The holy man explained that he would keep those envelopes overnight and in the morning, in the presence of all others who would want a similar service, he would perform the miracle for the four already selected.

The news of his offer spread like wildfire. Within minutes people began to gather in the square facing the old inn, to grab vantage points for the next morning. They kept coming all through the night and by early morning the square was jammed. Neighbor was fighting neighbor and brother was jostling brother for a place, amid squabbles and bitter arguments.

As the time for the appearance of the holy man neared, tempers flared up, one family fought another, and all wanted to be in the front row so as to beseech the holy man in one's own behalf. At last the holy man came out. An audible sigh swept quickly across the tightly packed square, and new squabbles began.

The holy man signaled for order, asked the four who gave him the sealed blank envelopes the night before to step forward, bowed his head in a short silent prayer and then said:

"My good people! The Lord on High, blessed be His name, saw fit to grant me certain privileges. I use them seldom, but because you were so insistent last night and are so eager this morning, I shall try to perform what you call a miracle. I cannot take anyone's cross away but I can make trades among those of you who want to change places with someone else. That is what I did for the four who turned in their envelopes last night . . ."

He stopped talking and handed an envelope to each of the four facing him. For a while there was a stunned silence but soon the recipients, pointing one at the other, began to cry and lament: "Oh no, oh no! I don't want his burdens. . . . I don't want his troubles. . . . I don't want her pains. . . . How was I to know his miseries? I'm better off in so many ways. . . . I don't want to change with him. . . . Please, holy man, let me have my own back again! . . . I'll be much happier with my own lot. . . ."

They grabbed his coat, pushed the envelopes and sheets of paper back at him and clutched at his arms in a frantic effort to regain what they had. The holy man shook his head with a sad mien and said: "I cannot undo what you asked me to do. That is not within my power. From now on you will have to bear your new crosses and shoulder your exchanged burdens . . . But perhaps some of those around you will want to change places with you. Ask your friends, neighbors or members of your family to step forward and I'll try to make the desired exchanges. . . ."

A wave of apprehension swept through the milling crowd as the townspeople, fearful of being called upon, hurried to scatter. Within minutes the square was empty of wishers and onlookers and only the hapless four, clutching crumbled sheets of paper, were left behind.

Is there a moral to the story? It is up to you to decide. One thing is certain, appearances can be deceiving. There is no quicker way to needless misery and unhappiness than to let envy, greed and avarice fill your heart and your thoughts. They are the implacable enemies of peace and contentment. They warp all good thought and corrupt decent, friendly feeling. Like a malignant cancer they feed greedily upon themselves and wax fat on jealousy and resentment.

Of course, there are some among those you know who are richer, better situated or more influential than you. Of course, there are some, even among your closest friends, who are better looking or more prominent than you. Of course, there are some who seem to be healthier or more fortunate than you, who appear to have so much more than you. But, you have no way of knowing the ailments they may have or the miseries they suffer.

You may be better off, physically if not financially, mentally if not materially, emotionally if not physically, than any other person you know, but for one reason or another you overlook it and still envy the other fellow. Perhaps you ought to be thankful and grateful for what you are and for what you have. Perhaps before you go to sleep tonight you ought to count your blessings and be thankful to Him for the cross you have to bear.

Perhaps that is what prompted Susan Curtis to pray:

"Dear Lord, forgive my sinful, foolish fears,
And give me daily, strengthening peace, I pray;
And one more thing I ask, with humble tears,
Take not my own cross away."

# CHAPTER EIGHT

# How to Deal With an Obsession

To be obsessed is to be in the power of an overwhelming desire, emotion, passion or belief. Thus, in a sense, anyone who is autotarian in his attitudes, rabid in his zeal, fiery in his fanaticism or immovable in his stand on a given subject, can be looked upon as one obsessed.

Obsessions, as odd and strange forms of behavior, were considered harmful, not to the person afflicted but to those around him. A person who began to act strangely and completely out of character, who was unpredictable in his actions and behavior or who did not conform to established modes and practices, was said to be possessed. It was believed that a devil had entered his body and to drive the devil out many strange rites were used. Among them were weird incantations, special brews, deafening noisemakers to scare the devil, and exorcisms. These practices usually failed to do much good and in order to isolate the obsessed one from the rest he was often incarcerated in a prison together with criminals, mental defectives and other unfortunates. And, if he showed any signs of violence he was chained to the walls of the cell. These deplorable practices were in use, among civilized nations, as late as the eighteenth century.

We act differently these days. We know now that an obsession is of mental origin, that it may be due to a delusion, to an entrenched fixation, or to a persistently recurring compulsion. In its milder form it may be a simple complex or an oversensitivity. The person thus affected may react normally to everything else but to a particular subject or situation.

He may consciously suppress his obsession and it may manifest itself in other ways. It may bring about insomnia, gas pains, colitis, headaches, melancholy and digestive disturbances. They, in turn, may lead to asthma, to rheumatism, to nervous indigestion, to high blood pressure, to heart trouble or to glandular disorders.

If the basic sources of the irritants are not removed and the obsession is allowed to entrench itself it may lead to serious mental ailments. But such mental aberrations are not within the scope of this book. If, however, you are aware of your compulsion or obsession and feel that by knowing some of the underlying reasons you could offset the effects upon you, then the following may prove helpful to you.

One form of obsession common among older people is the resurge to childish fears and superstitions. You may be harboring such beliefs and may be suffering from their effects upon you. For instance, do you consider it unlucky to walk under a ladder, to see your shadow by the light of the moon, to cross the path of a black cat, to break a mirror or to do anything on a Friday which happens to fall on the thirteenth of the month?

Do you believe in ghosts or are afraid of the dark? Do you believe that a horseshoe, a charm, an amulet, a rabbit's foot, a four leaf clover or the tooth of a tiger will ward off evil and bring you good luck? Are you afraid of the "evil eye," the curse of a blind man, the mutterings of a gypsy or the mumbo-jumbo of witches? Do you honestly believe that anyone can foretell your future and therefore you must follow his prognostications?

Superstition is synonymous with belief although the two have little in common. Belief is the acceptance of something that is real, true, trustworthy. It is an act of the mind, the assent to something that is genuine and authoritative. It is conviction arrived at through reasoning, whether or not such is confirmed by proof. It is akin to trust, to abiding faith.

Superstition, on the other hand, is supposition. It is fear for the unknown. It is credulity built up by incident or deliberate design. It is induced reverence for the unknown, for the mystifying, for things which one cannot explain or understand. It is the irrational belief in the power of the sun, in the destructive forces of the wind, in the punishment imbedded in the heat of fire, in the noise of the thunder and the lightning that strikes from the sky. It is often deliberately contrived by those in power, through the supposed influence of charms, omens, signs, magic, strange incantations and weird contortions or pronouncements.

One of the reasons why superstition influences many people lies in their desire to find a form of security, to reach a semblance of wish fulfillment, to bolster their hopes and aspirations. The promises made by fortune tellers, the powers supposedly shown by signs or held by omens, the guesses or suppositions advanced by soothsayers, the hope fostered by brews and potions, the expectations engendered by incantations of mystifying rites, build up the disposition to believe. As such, they become a palliative medium, a temporary escape from reality, a reaching out for one's dream. Unfortunately, they carry with them an inherent danger, the tendency to rely upon them and guide one's conduct accordingly.

This is where you have to be on guard. Learn to take all mystic readings, glib prognostications, glimpses into the future, signs, charms and omens in a light vein. Accept them in the way you take the characters, the plots and the situations in a story or a play. No one can possibly foretell anyone else's future. He can deduce or surmise, imagine or rationalize, assume or venture so-called predictions. But he cannot know what may happen tomorrow or one hour from now, insofar as you or he himself are concerned. Look upon such acts as diversions, as fancies of the imagination, and then they will add to your pleasures of living.

Another form of obsession is a fear built up into a compulsion. You may or may not be aware of it as such, but here is how one psychiatrist suggests ways to uncover the compulsion and to deal with it.

1—Start putting down on paper for the next two or three weeks, using a separate sheet for each day, all the things you do, without omitting anything no matter how trivial it might be.

2—Underline the things you must do, the things you *like* to do and the things you *dislike* doing in different ways, with special emphasis on the things you do because something drives you or compels you to do them.

3—Segregate the things you keep doing against your will or your better judgment, that are senseless or make you feel miserable, that arouse quarrels or foster misunderstandings, that harm you, set you back or make you suffer needlessly. Trace their beginning if possible, especially to what happens immediately before or afterwards.

4—Group those before-and-after effects as close as you can, even if there is no connection between them and try to get at the basic, underlying reasons.

5—Begin to trace those reasons as far back as you can and look for the tie-ins, for the connecting links. In other words, try to find out why, how, when and where your compulsion got its start.

This five-step checkback may help you to uncover the original beginning of the compulsion. That, in turn, will facilitate your ability to counteract its influence upon you and gradually eliminate it in these ways:

1—If you recognized the compulsion, give it its real name. Identify it for what it is, as a way to mitigate a real or fancied wrong, as a form of expiation or self-punishment, as a method to allay pricks of conscience or to ease a feeling of guilt.

2—Expose its seemingly senseless tie-up and purposes to the bright light of day. Call the compulsion by its real name. Show what it hides, what it stands for, what it tries to cover up.

3—Let the exposure be deliberate. It is a form of self-confession intended only for your own eyes and ears. So—do not hide, color or justify the true implications of the compulsion and the things you have been doing to carry it through.

4—Look for ways to ridicule, to belittle, to offset and to minimize the foolish urge to cover up something that needs to be corrected, something that bothers you and finds expression in the compulsion.

5—Plan your day's activities, at work, at home, at play or whatever you might be doing and wherever you might be

in a manner that will make it difficult, foolish, undesirable
or impossible for you to follow your compulsion or obsession
for the time being.

6—Redirect and rearrange your activities wherever possible, so that you may be forced to do the exact opposite of
what you have been doing under the influence of your obsession. This will take a little time and will power on your part
but it is sure to bring the desired results.

The analysis suggested and the steps given to follow
through in your aims to offset the existing obsession will be
as good and effective as the honesty of your efforts. If you
go about it half-heartedly, if you justify your old actions
and routines, if you give excuses or alibis, you will defeat
the purposes of this analysis.

Treat the procedures as objectively as you can. Think of
yourself as a close friend of someone dear to you, someone
who has confidence in you, someone who asked you to "put
your finger" on his troublesome obsession. In other words,
face the facts frankly, honestly, and do no shirk "telling on
yourself."

If you cannot go about it conscientiously in the open self-
analysis form, try the free association method. Isolate yourself somewhere, away from any interruptions, and start putting down on paper whatever comes to your mind. Try to
transfer your stream of aimless, purposeless thinking onto
paper. Put down everything that comes to your mind, no
matter how irrelevant it might be. Keep at it constantly for
twenty or thirty minutes a day until the writing comes easy
and true.

Let this writing be a confession, a baring of your soul,
a frank diary, a literal pouring out of all your hurts, desires,

wishes, grievances and resentments. Use names, dates, places, details, and do not mask your true feelings and reactions. No one else will see this confession of yours. Hence, you do not have to hide details or disguise the facts.

Of course, no matter how honest you might want to be, you will seek to "whitewash" your feelings and justify your desires at first. But this tendency will gradually disappear as you continue to write and as you deliberately put down your innermost thoughts, your hidden urges, your amoral urges, your repressions and resentments. Soon, the writing will come easier. Before long, the mere exposure of the things that trouble you will become a catharsis.

All of this will gradually reveal the basic reasons why you have an obsession or why you feel compelled to do certain incomprehensible things. For instance, you may be one of those who has to clear his throat several times before saying something to a given person or addressing a group. Or, you may be one of those who hastens to wash his hands every time someone happens to brush against him or touch him in some casual way. With the knowledge why you have to do it will come understanding of how to cope with and how to eliminate the obsession.

# CHAPTER NINE

# Help Yourself to Better Mental Health

Raymond Johnson never had to shoulder responsibility. As a child and as a youngster his parents sheltered him in every way and made living easy for him. He was never called upon to make a decision because there were always others ready to act for him, willing to assume the risks and bear the consequences.

After his graduation from high school his father took him into the hardware business, paying him a salary for doing nothing. He had no special duties or responsibilities and spent most of the working time outside of the store. Three or four years later when a second cousin, Elaine, came to spend her summer vacation with them, they were thrown together a great deal and somehow became engaged and were married within a year.

Before the first twelve months passed by Elaine bore him a child. Raymond left the boy's upbringing to the mother and to the proud grandparents. Once again he escaped shouldering any responsibility. Time went on. Raymond's father had a sudden heart attack and passed away a few weeks later. The management of the business was taken over by the senior clerk and somehow it continued to go on without Raymond's direct management.

Nothing new came up within the next few years to necessitate action on his part. Raymond grew older and so did his family. Then his mother passed away and his wife died of double pneumonia, but his son married in the meantime and somehow they moved in with him, sharing the big house he inherited, and providing him with the care he needed.

Once again life ran smoothly for Raymond. He passed his 60th birthday and was set for many comfortable years. But his childless daughter-in-law gave birth to a son and no longer had the time to cater to the old man's wishes and desires. He was confused at first and bewildered, then grew incensed and demanded the old-time care and attention. He threatened to take away the house, to shut the son out of the business, to do things to himself, but all of his pleas and threats availed him nothing.

He found himself alone in a strange, forbidding world, a world that cared little for him, and grew terribly afraid of the days to come. He was never before called upon to rely upon himself or to do things for himself. He could not face the future by himself and had to find a way out. Mysterious pains assailed him and strange visions came to him again and again. Soon afterwards he escaped into a private world of his own, a world where once again he was a child, with other people to tend to his wants and provide for his needs. He found new joys and pleasures in his new world, although it was an institution and there was a long medical term to identify his mental condition.

Raymond was not prepared to face life in his youth and could not cope with life in his old age. His was a lost cause, but what about you? Have you retained the questioning spirit, the desire to learn new things and accept the new challenges of life? There is so much to be learned, so much to be gained, when you train yourself to look upon life as a series of episodes, as mileposts in your journey through life, some pleasant, others not so pleasant and even painful.

You may not be able to retain your youthful vigor, maintain your earlier drives or be as active as you were, but you can add much to your well-being and your enjoyment when you learn how to adapt yourself, mentally and emotionally, to your advancing years.

Think of your age in its various aspects. (1) In its chronological sense, based upon your calendar years. They, in themselves, are not and should not be the measure of your abilities, capacities, usefulness and potentialities. Some people are old at forty and others are still young at seventy. You may be one of those who grows with his age and therefore will never be old.

(2) In its biological sense. From the standpoint of your organic functions and your medical history you may be many years younger than someone else in the same age group. (3) In the social sense, as evidenced by your self-evaluation and by your contacts with others. (4) In the intellectual aspect, as shown by your interests and activities. (5) In its emotional aspects, as measured by your attitudes, reactions and general behavior.

Of course, important changes have taken place in you. Life made huge demands upon your mental and emotional reserves through the years and left its marks upon you. Those reserves may be depleted now and your past sins and omissions may be catching up with you.

Mention was made in a previous chapter of the abuses and mistreatments which you imposed upon your senses and organs through the years, and how such affect your physical conditions at this time. The same is true of your mental and emotional self. You may have to unlearn certain old ways of living and set aside many of your former habits, attitudes and pursuits.

Among those adjustments will be the acceptance of your older age and the restrictions it places upon you, the readiness to "let go" of habitual activities harmful to you in your present age, the willingness to live at peace with the inevitable changes in you and make the most of what you are and of what you can do within the limitations of your age.

All of these adjustments depend upon the cultivation of the proper feelings, for although they are intangible things they exercise a dominant influence upon you. Your feelings count a great deal. But what ARE feelings? The dictionary defines feeling as a sense impression, a response, a sensitivity, a tendency or a predilection. Thus, in a simple physical denotation, feeling is an impression that reached you through your senses and made you react in a certain manner. Your reaction, however, is the mental or the emotional response. That, in turn, is modified or amplified by your acceptance and interpretation.

Your feelings are the product of what you are and what you do, of what you think habitually and how you generally behave. It is part of the conditioning process that began with the day of your birth and was continually affected by your parental influences, your schooling, the status your family held in the community, the work you chose, the friends you made and the position you attained in your own name. In other words, your feelings and emotions are colored by and filtered by your concepts, thoughts, desires, beliefs, likes, opinions, convictions and even prejudices.

Those feelings and emotions become set in their impact upon you as you grow older. You may be the exception but most older people are loath to change, are unwilling to consider new ideas and are ever critical of things new and different. They prefer to leave matters as they were even though the new may be better and more desirable.

What is more, as an older person you are more susceptible to emotional disturbances. One of the reasons for it is in the fact that you have more time to think of and pay attention to your reactions. Another reason is in the gradual weakening of your resistance to petty annoyances and irritations. Still another is in your unwillingness to accept your advancing years and older age.

This book cannot and does not attempt to deal with emotional upsets, with mental maladjustments, with entrenched fixations or neuroses which come under the jurisdiction of psychiatrists or psychoanalysts. Its aim is only to indicate the ways in which wrong mental concepts start and how to avert or minimize them.

Your emotional upset may start with a fear which feeds upon itself and grows from day to day. Such fear can bring more suffering and cause more misery than any combination of sicknesses or adverse circumstances. A fear that feeds upon itself is like a malignancy. It develops rapidly into a neurosis. It may begin with only one induced feeling or reaction but it spreads quickly into different directions and before long other nonrelated feelings, emotions and reactions are affected. These lead to hypertension, various psychosomatic ailments and to eventual mental breakdown.

To offset the growing tensions, some people turn to tranquilizers and to other anti-depressant pills. But the promiscuous use of such pills is dangerous. At their best they are only stop-gaps. They can provide only a temporary relief and as one's system gets used to them they lose their effectiveness and shorten the relief period. To counteract such effect they have to be taken more frequently, thereby increasing the damage inflicted upon the sensory and the nervous systems. They cannot possibly get at the underlying irritants and remove the causes for the existing emotional disturbance.

To paraphrase a passage from *How to Conquer Fears, Worries and Frustrations in 30 Hours,* "Your mental reaction to fear is the father to the physical preparation to fight, to run away or to seek safety in some other manner. The pattern of a 'fear behavior' goes through these five stages. (1) The awareness of the imminent peril or danger. (2) The desire to fight, to avoid or to escape the pending danger. (3) The physical response to the mental concept. (4) The aroused disagreeable feelings or sensations. (5) The search for relief, for escape or for safety. Find the way to offset or to counteract any one of these five stages and the fear will not develop."

A fear often starts inauspiciously. It begins with a simple or a compound feeling, with something which you experienced before and have forgotten or with something entirely new. It may have no direct bearing upon the immediate situation or circumstance. But, because of the time or the place, the circumstance or association of ideas, the people involved or the mood engendered, the feeling brings an intense reaction. It turns into a sudden paralyzing fear that quickens your heartbeat and makes you tremble with an inexplicable growing dread. You have an agonizing moment of panic and somehow the feeling and the fear merge into one. They become inseparable so that one invokes the other and sets up the fear complex.

You refuse to accept the fear in itself without tying it in

with something specific. Knowing that heart trouble is one of the chief killers of our times you begin to listen, with a trace of deep anxiety, to your heart beat. It thumps louder and beats faster than you have ever heard before and you immediately assume that you had a heart-attack warning. You decide to watch your heart action from that moment on, and strangely enough, at least in your mind's eye, your heart begins to play up.

Now, new worries and anxieties step into the picture. They throw your digestion, your sleeping habits and your normal reactions to the ordinary discomforts of each day completely out of line. You become sensitized to minor inconveniences, grow impatient with people, give way to depressive moods or lash out at everybody and everything in sight. You develop nervous tensions and edginess. They keep you at high pitch, pump more adrenal into your system, speed your heart action and that, in turn, intensifies your fear. The vicious circle is now completed and unless steps are taken to counteract your newly formed mental concept and your newly formed fear you are in for a host of psychosomatic ailments with all the pain and the misery they entail.

What are some of the ways to cope with that condition? Here are ten of them, based partially on "A Decalogue of Health for Senior Citizens," as developed by the geriatrician, Dr. George W. Ainley, Sr., and on excerpts from *How to Conquer Fears, Worries and Frustrations in 30 Hours*.

### 1. Avoid Needless Emotional Upsets

A. An angry or defiant attitude, a belligerent behavior, an arbitrary argumentative tendency or needless frictions at home, can greatly affect your mental health and bring emotional upsets.

If you are a man past 65 who retired only recently and "hang around" your house too much, you may be keeping your wife on edge and adding needlessly to your own unrest. You are retired but she is not. She is burdened with your being at home, under foot as it were, and has to cater to you morning, noon and night. So—find things to do *away* from home, try to give her a rest. You will be eliminating heartaches for her and adding to your pleasures.

If you are the wife of a man who retired recently from regular work and is still at "sixes and sevens," help him to adjust himself to his enforced idleness. Tolerate his interferences with your home chores for the time being. Be the wiser and the smarter of the two. Help him to look for and to find new contacts and interests. Join him in some of those things even if you have to pretend. Build up his ego and let him feel he is still your one and only love.

If you are the child of a parent who lives with you, who has not as yet adjusted himself to his enforced retirement, who is irritable, demanding or inconsiderate and "strikes back" at you and your family, be the stronger of the two for the time being. Let his anger flow over you and try to meet him halfway or all the way if necessary to maintain peace. In the meantime, help him look for and find new interests, new contacts and outlets. Things will change and the "oldster" will eventually find himself.

B. As an older person living alone, with your wife or your children, give them the benefit of the doubt and do not try their patience too much. Look for contacts and interests which will bring you pleasures and relaxation. If some of those with whom you associate annoy you, try to avoid them, or drop them altogether. If some of your activities tire you or displease you, drop them. Look instead for those pastimes and recreations which will add something to your daily life and thus prevent needless emotional upsets.

C. Do not assume duties or obligations in your social or communal life just because you have the time, are looking for commendation or cannot refuse gracefully. Know your limitations and stay well within them. Be willing to help, to cooperate, to take an active part in different things. Work for a cause or on some long-time project with other people, but remember your age, and never allow those activities to take a heavy toll of your physical capacity and your reserves of energy.

### 2. Seek Suitable Recreational Activities

A. Look for things to do, at home or elsewhere, that interest you and are suitable to your age and abilities. This does not imply that you should not try your hand at something new and different from your customary activities.

B. If you developed a heart condition or some other disabilities which restrict your active particiation in favorite pastimes you may have to reorientate and rehabilitate yourself. This is where you may need expert help and guidance. This may also prove to be a blessing in disguise because you may uncover talents and abilities of value and importance to you and to others.

### 3. Cultivate a Feeling of Security

A. Think of your living quarters, no matter how modest they may be, as your sanctuary, your haven of rest and tranquility. You can surround it with an aura of respect and privacy, with a sense of values and importance, even if it is only a room in someone else's house.

B. Do not demean or debase yourself because you have

reached the retirement age, because you no longer work steadily at a given job or because you do not have your old-time vigor and vitality. The years of your life have given you knowledge, experience, background and maturity of judgment which cannot be discounted or set aside. They add weight and stability to your opinions and conclusions.

C. Place a value upon yourself as a parent, as a wife or a husband, as a friend or a neighbor, as a mature human being who is entitled to respect and consideration. Whatever your station in life may have been you contributed your share, in work and in money, in thought and in effort, in support and direction, to life around you, throughout the years. You were and still are an important member of your family circle, a citizen of your community, a voice in the affairs of your town and county, and your opinion and participation within those spheres of contact still count. So—retain and maintain your feeling of security and do not undersell yourself.

## 4. Develop a Sense of Humor

A. Learn to look for and to see the humorous side of a given situation, even when everything looks black and forbidding. Nothing is so bad that it could not be worse or that does not lend itself to improvement. Nothing can be so solemn and serious as not to have its lighter moments or redeeming features. This does not imply that you should turn into a Pollyanna, that "all is for the best in this best of all possible worlds," but rather that you should not "go to pieces" when something happens to you and do the best you can under the circumstances.

B. Cultivate the ability to laugh, even at your own expense. It is amazing how quickly a ready laugh eases a bad situation and how it lightens a boresome and burdensome task.

## 5. Seek Desirable Companionships

A. Age, sex, looks, background or position in life have no special importance in making and keeping friends. It is not who you are but what you are. You build friendships by what you do and say, by your attitudes and reactions, by the attention you give to others and the respect you have for their views and opinions, by your willingness to cooperate with others and the consideration you give to their rights and sensibilities.

B. Friendship is a reciprocal process. It does not grow by itself. You have to cultivate it and give it room to bloom. You have to give of yourself first before others will meet you along the way. This is as true today as it ever was and will work for you at any time and at all times.

## 6. Leave Your Mind Open

A. A closed mind is like a self-made prison where you stay in solitary confinement. Every prejudice, every preconceived notion becomes another portion of a wall separating you from the outside world. You must leave your mind open to a difference of opinion and to a possible disagreement with your views and ideas. You may have the wrong slant on a given thing or may not be aware of pending or actual changes which may have a strong bearing upon the subject matter. What is more, the changes suggested may supplement your own idea and make it all the more valuable, workable or desirable.

B. An open mind makes you receptive to changes and helps you to change with those that are inevitable. An open mind lets you consider the ideas of other people, which may be contrary to your own, without placing them beforehand on your personal judgment block and without the formation of hasty conclusions.

### 7. Be Ever Curious

A. One of the sure ways to retain an interest in life around you and maintain an alert mind is never to take things for granted, but be forever curious. You are never too old to ask questions and to learn. Many new ideas, discoveries and developments have taken place all around you within the last few years. Have you ever stopped to ask what they are and how they came about? Do any of them hold any particular interest for you? If so, has that interest been satisfied? It not, why not?

B. Try to learn how and why changes have taken place in you? Why has your hair turned gray? Why is your vision not as good as it was years ago? Why is your hearing impaired? What causes hardening of the arteries? Why do you have to be more careful in your food intake, in your habits and various activities? Why are you more irritable now than ever before? Why do you have periods of mild depression? Why do some older people become childish and careless in their toilet habits? Why do some people age more than others? What steps should you take to engender a better mental attitude toward yourself and in your contacts with others?

These and other similar questions should interest you. Look for the right answers to them in books taken from your local library, in classes available to you at your adult schools and from specialists in the respective fields. Then, and only then, will you widen your vision, add to your knowledge and understanding.

### 8. Enrich Your Spiritual Life

The ennobling value of abiding faith and spiritual belief can add a greater, deeper meaning to your life. As J. G. Holland put it so beautifully: ". . . we build the ladder by

which we rise upward . . . a noble deed is a step toward
God . . ." Build your ladder step by step toward higher,
nobler things, toward a better understanding of yourself and
your fellow men.

Take more time to read, to absorb and to live by the words
and the teachings of our sages, thinkers, philosophers and
spiritual leaders. Look for those gems of wisdom at your
nearest public library. Adapt them to your way of living.
Put into practice the ideas which appeal to you and let them
add to your stature.

Become an "opsimath." Take up studies of things you
like in the free day and evening classes available to you at
your local adult schools. Many people past age 65 are doing
it. This trend is so pronounced that a new term was coined
for it. It is "opsimathy," meaning education obtained late
in life, and it is yours for the asking.

## 9. Acquire a Handicraft Activity

A. Whether or not you worked with your hands at your
former profession or occupation you will gain in mental
health and in emotional stability by learning how to do something satisfying with your hands in your leisure time. Let it
be in the arts and crafts where you can be creative with wood
or metal, with pen or crayon, with paint and brushes, with
cloth or leather, with clay or wire, with tile or terra-cotta.

You can join a class at your nearest center, senior adult
group or adult school, where others in your age group with
little or no experience are finding new ways to enjoy their
leisure hours and at the same time satisfy their urge for self-
expression.

B. If you prefer not to join others and work at something
by yourself, you can take up gardening, horticulture, wood-

turning, embossing, hand carving, book binding or gadget making. The various hobby shops in your community will be glad to show you how to go about it and provide all the tools and materials needed.

## 10. Set a Goal or a Purpose for Yourself

A. Take up a long-range program in keeping with your dreams and interests. Perhaps you would like to study something you always wanted to learn but could never get around to it. Now, with time on your hands, there is no reason why you could not attend adult classes and take up the studies or education you missed.

B. Perhaps you would like to learn how to play a musical instrument. If so, why not follow through? Join a music class at the nearest adult school or get a few other people together to form a small group and engage a teacher. You may never gain fame and glory as a concert musician but you are sure to have many hours of pleasure as you learn to coordinate your hands and your mind in playing a given musical instrument.

C. Perhaps you would like to espouse a certain cause. You may feel that the blind or the handicapped, the teen-agers or the crippled children, the needy or the shut-ins, the displaced or the mentally disturbed in your community do not get the proper help and attention from the existing services and social agencies.

You can do something about it, either as a determined citizen who takes it upon himself to call matters to the attention of the proper authorities, or as a member of a group that sets up such cause as its primary objective. And, if such group does not operate in your locality or is not active enough in its basic purposes you could assume the initiative to start a new group or reactivate the old and correct matters to your satisfaction.

D. Perhaps you would prefer to devote your time to church work. As an elderly man or woman you may find it most rewarding to teach Sunday school, to promote the building of a new social hall, to visit shut-ins, to serve as companion to a disabled member or perhaps help spread the word of God.

The ten general ways suggested are but a few of the guideposts that can help you stay young and alert in mind, no matter how many calendar years are added to your age. You can take up one or several of them and in so doing there will be no time for you to fret or to worry about little aches and pains or about the visible manifestations of your advancing years.

The zeal for living a full life and for retaining a healthy mental outlook is not measured by your calendar years and is not conditioned by your sex, looks, build, knowledge, background and circumstances. It is in how you feel, in how you act, in how you respond and in how you adjust yourself to life within you and around you. They are the things you can control at any time, at any place and at all times.

By reaching your present age you outlived many others who were not granted the privilege to live on. Your chances to reach a still riper age are now better than they ever were. But such longevity places certain responsibilities upon you. Among them are: (1) To retain and maintain your physical and mental well-being as long as possible. (2) To leave the past behind you and bring into the present only those things you wish to remember. (3) To accept the limitations of your age without rancor or regrets. (4) To take advantage of every

opportunity to add joys and satisfaction to everyday living.
(5) To give freely of yourself to those who can benefit by
what you know and what you can do.

If you are married, you and your spouse no longer have
the cares and worries of earlier years and you can age gracefully together in close companionship. You have no children
to rear and no need to set something aside for the future. It
is here, now, and what you get out of it is entirely up to you.
Now is the time for you to enjoy your golden age, and in your
togetherness find joys, comforts and understanding through
the days and years yet to come.

If you lost your spouse somewhere along the way, your
chances to remarry and to find love, sympathy and companionship with someone else are greater than ever. Literally
thousands of men and women faced the same situation and
marriages between those in their golden age take place by
the hundreds every day of the year.

The older person who remarries and learns how to adapt
himself to the new spouse has a greater expectancy of life
and a far better chance to reach a riper old age than the un-
married one. This is true for both men and women in all
walks of life and is due to many physiological and psycho-
logial reasons. So—if you lost your mate, are a confirmed
bachelor or a seemingly satisfied spinster, it might pay you
to change your views and look around. Expose yourself to
the possibilities of finding someone of the opposite sex with
whom you could share your interests and your activities. Then
living may become much sweeter and happier for you.

As Americans, we lead too fast a life. We are forever "on
the run," always seeking to save a minute or two, always
trying to be as good or better than our neighbors. We do it
at a terrific cost in emotional strain and nervous tension. This

mad pace, this constant hustle starts in our teens and before
long becomes an entrenched habit. Hence, when we reach the
retirement age we still follow the same maddening pace; we
still continue the same hurry, flurry and scurry, at great harm
to our physical and nervous systems.

Your doctor and your common sense will tell you that
as you grow older you have to slow down and take things
easier. You have to learn to accept the encroachment of old
age with all of its transitions. You also have to avoid the
tendency to look upon each new birthday as another step
closer to your death.

Introspection and retrospection, indulged in too freely
and too often, can lead only to misery and unhappiness. Stop
torturing yourself for the things you did or did not do in the
past. Live now as best as you can and make every moment
count. Develop the inner capacity to be good company to yourself and cultivate the faculty of adapting yourself to the
people and the conditions around you.

Perhaps one of the first steps toward a healthy mental outlook upon your older age is to avoid making a fetish of and
paying homage to youth. Act your age and do not ape youth
in your dress, in your make-up and in your behavior, to become a comic figure. Youthful lines and contours have their
"sure-fire" appeal but there is also charm and beauty in gray
hair and in faces lined with life. Such lines often bespeak
more kindness, goodness, gentleness, interest and friendliness
than smooth, vapid, unlined features.

Older age carries with it dignity, wisdom, knowledge,
maturity, judgment, tolerance, repose and understanding
which only years of living can bring and which no superficial
youthfulness can match. Capitalize upon those qualities and

you will never need to feel subservient or apologetic to any-one for your matured age.

Growing older gracefully, peacefully, happily, is a way of living which you can instigate and cultivate. It is in knowing how best to utilize your abilities and capacities. It is in learning how to evaluate and to appreciate, even in your own estimation, the things you can do well. It is in adopting a way of thinking, of changing your perspectives, of learning to see life around you in a new light.

For instance, here is the concept of the world in its relation to himself as William Brighty Rands saw it:

"Great, wide, beautiful, wonderful world,
With all the wonderful water around you curled,
And the wonderful grass upon your breast,
World, you are beautifully dressed.
The wonderful air is over me,
And the wonderful wind is shaking the tree;
It walks on the water and whirls the mills,
And talks to itself on the top of the hills.
You, friendly Earth! How far do you go
With wheat fields that nod and rivers that flow,
With cities and gardens, and cliffs and isles,
And people upon you for hundreds of miles?
Ah, you are so good, and I am so small,
I tremble to think of you, World, at all;
And yet, when I said my prayers today,
A whisper in me seemed to say:
'You are more than the Earth, tho' only a dot,
You can love and think and the Earth can not!' "

Yes, you can love, laugh, think, dream, work, build, live and enjoy life in so many different ways if you but expose yourself to the good and the wonderful around you.

You have many things in your favor, and if you are not sure of what they are, make an inventory of your physical and mental capacities. Do it by listing on several sheets of paper, one by one, the abilities you have, the knowledge you accumulated, the experience you have, the good points you possess, the skills you know, the home you made, the family you raised, the friends you have, and the many ways in which you contributed to life around you. Add to this the contacts you made, the interests you can follow and the many opportunities you have now to enjoy your leisure time.

Now take other sheets of paper and beginning with the first, headed "Liabilities" or "Disadvantages," list in detail all of your infirmities, disabilities, limitations and the things you cannot do any longer. Then check the first set of sheets against the second and later compare your inventory with the status of other people you know in your age group and in your financial standing.

Do this audit honestly, consicentiously, and it may be a revelation to you. It may remind you of all the good you did through the years, engender a greater sense of self-esteem because of your contributions to life around you, foster within you a deeper sense of well-being and accomplishment and promote better mental health. It may also serve to impress upon you how well off you are in comparison to others and how many ways there are for you to maintain better mental health.

Now, supposing you wanted to instill the same sense of well-being and the same sense of accomplishment in others. Supposing you wanted to help someone else to take better care of his aging parents, what are the steps to be taken? You or they would have to follow some of the suggestions already given and at the same time keep in mind the following possible exigencies:

1—The knowledge that many an older person is sensitive. He is quick to take offense or feel hurt. As a rule he does not want to be coddled like a child or be treated like a foolish or crotchety oldster. He wants to be useful, to feel that someone wants him or cares for him and at the same time he wants to be free to lead his own life.

2—The awareness that many an older person "puts much store" in the simple everyday "creature comforts." In some instances those are the only things left for him to enjoy. So— do the most you can to provide those needs for him.

3—The fact that many an older person often grows careless in his habits, heedless of the need for personal hygiene and indifferent to the necessity of following simple sanitary precautions in his daily life. He may need prompting or coaching along those lines.

4—The understanding that many an older person often loses his sense of balance and standards of value. He may trip easily, fall and injure himself. He may gulp his food and can easily choke on a large bite. He may eat too much and later have indigestion or suffer from poor elimination. He may need watching in those respects.

5—The awareness that some older people tend to build up groundless suspicions and animosities. They attach undue importance to whatever possessions they have and are ever fearful lest those things be taken from them. They hasten to hide some of these things in the most unlikely places and when such cannot be found later are quick to accuse the people around them of stealing.

6—The knowledge that many an older person has a wandering mind and occasional lapses of memory. He will forget to blow out a match but will readily blow out a gas flame. He will leave drawers wide open, scatter his belongings on the floor and trip over them afterwards. He will ignore traffic signals, step off curbs without looking and often endanger his own life as well as the lives of those around him. He may need constant watching in that respect.

7—The fact that older people always crave care, service or attention. They will go to great lengths in their desire to achieve those ends and have tantrums and sick spells. They will readily cry on the shoulder of any person willing to listen to their tall tales and will often accuse their friends and relatives of abuse and mistreatments.

8—On the other hand, many an older person needs only a kind word, a show of interest in him, a token of sympathy, a chance to do something or be useful in some way so as to retain his mental balance and his self-assurance. Find out how to do those things for the older person whom you want to help and you will have his undying gratitude.

You, too, may need some of those helps to add to the fullness and richness of your life. If so, you can help yourself to better mental health by seeking self-expression through work, play, love, learning, study and spiritual faith. You can have better mental health by taking an interest in other people, by letting others confide in you, by taking an active part in various activities of interest to you, by joining group discussions of mutual problems, by being ready and willing to do things for others, by sharing the things you know and the things you enjoy with others. You can have better mental health by learning to be amiable, friendly and quick to overlook common failings and minor discrepancies.

Follow these things consistently, deliberately, knowingly, day after day, and you will surely find the gold in your golden age.

# CHAPTER TEN

# How to Supplement Your Income

If you were a professional man or woman or were self-employed before your retirement and now must supplement your income you face no problem. You go back to work and give as much or as little time to it as you want or need.

But if you were a worker in a plant, if you were a mere "cog-in-the-wheel" in a mass production line and your age now is an impassable barrier to re-employment, and if on top of that you have no special skills or abilities and yet must supplement your income, you face a real problem. Your problem may be aggravated even more if you are disabled in any way and cannot take up work as casually as in years past.

To find better ways on how to meet such a problem let us consider it along these lines: (1) How to Look for and Find a Full-time Job. (2) How to Get Part-time Work. (3) How to Start a Small Business. (4) How to Develop Sources of Income. (5) How to Secure Old Age Assistance, Social Security Benefits or other financial help from the Social Agencies.

### How to Find a Full-time Job

The first thing to remember is that you cannot compete in the open market for the same job, side by side, with those who are considerably younger than you. You stand very little chance to be hired because although you may look young, feel young and are confident of your ability to meet the requirements, your age will be against you. Few employers, even when inclined to favor you, can accept you at your own evaluation.

Present union and Social Security requirements bar you completely from many jobs and you will incur only heartache by trying to break those restrictions. Then, there are other types of jobs which "rule" you out, especially if they call for dexterity or youthful vigor.

You have to look for the kind of job where in lieu of dexterity, agility, youthfulness, stamina, ambition and the readiness to work for the future you can offer dependability or experience which only years of on-the-job work can bring.

With these things in mind, take an account of your values. Make a detailed inventory of those abilities and qualifications that would interest a prospective employer and go about it in these ways:

1—Sit down somewhere, away from possible interference, place several sheets of paper before you and start with number one. List in chronological order, starting with the last job you held, all the jobs you held during your life. Enumerate the things you did, the skills you acquired, the abilities you displayed, the qualifications you have, the formal and on-the-job schooling you had, and elaborate upon your special accomplishments that brought recognition or promotion.

If you held executive positions as your climbed from the bottom, list the ramifications of your duties and responsibilities. Stress particularly the problems you faced and how you met them, the difficulties you had and how you overcame them and the plans and ideas you originated to enhance your values as an executive. Try to be specific in each case. Give names, places, dates, before and after results, and wherever possible, supply recorded proof of accomplishment, such as press clippings, letters of appreciation and commendation.

2—List on other sheets of paper your various hobbies, your leisure time activities, your special interests, your membership in different groups and organizations with special emphasis on such activities where you held office, met certain problems, overcame certain difficulties, instigated certain plans of operation, promoted given projects and secured desired results. Here, too, be specific. Give names, dates, places and full details substantiated by newspaper or other clippings, by letters, citations or other evidences of your accomplishments.

The things you did as a member or an officer of a given group could conceivably be applied in solving problems in the business world, and the pastimes you followed in your leisure hours may also be converted into job-making opportunities. If you gained certain knowledge as a collector, if you can polish semi-precious stones, work in clay or mosaics, tool leather, emboss copper, weave rugs, knit sweaters, crossbreed flowers or fashion fancy cookies, they could become your springboard for a job.

3—Having enumerated the jobs you held, the skills you acquired, the experience you gained, the results you achieved and the special activities you followed where you met adverse conditions and circumstances, begin to list on another sheet of paper all the jobs suggested by your lists, over and above the regular work you followed most of the time.

With the list of jobs that you can handle placed before

you, begin to check it against trade papers and against your classified telephone directory and put down on paper all companies within the same or allied fields who could conceivably use your services. Mark down especially the smaller and newer firms and below each name list all the reasons you can give why your services would be useful and valuable to that company.

4—For your next step, list on a new sheet of paper all of your fixed and variable expenses, including a reserve fund for possible medical expenses and unexpected contingencies. Check it against the total income you have at this time. The difference between the two itemized columns will be the minimum extra income you need to maintain your health and a decent standard of living.

5—Now, and this may be difficult to follow through since you have to do it objectively and impartially, put a vertical line across a new sheet of paper and for the moment assume the role of a prospective employer who is going to raise a number of objections to giving you a job. Put those objections down, one by one, to the left of the vertical line, and continue to list all the objections which could be raised.

Then, beginning on the right side of the vertical line, give the best and most plausible answers you can find. Let them be the kind of answers you would use if you were face-to-face with an employer who has just the job you want, the job you can fill. Let them be the kind of answers that would convince him that you are the best man for the job.

Keep on rewriting and refining those answers, supplement them with facts, dates, figures and other proofs that would carry weight, and memorize them. Your next step will be to evaluate the jobs you could fill, the amount of additional income you must have, and where you must concentrate your efforts to get the job best fitted to your needs and limitations.

Then, and only then, will you be ready to list your first, second and third preference in jobs and start a systematic check of every possibility in these ways:

1—To check newspaper and trade publication help-wanted columns, especially those which do not specify age limits, where your training, skills, experience and accumulated knowledge can be an important factor for your employment.

2—To contact the nearest department of employment of your county or state and list with that office the various jobs you could fill. Do the same thing at the Welfare Department for the Aged, the Old Age Assistance League and the Senior Citizens Service Center in your town.

3—Leave complete details about yourself and the type of jobs you could handle with one or more of the local private employment agencies. Let them charge you a fee for finding the job you want, provided it is to be paid only from the wages you receive.

4—If you were or still are a member in a union, have a heart-to-heart talk with the business agent in your locality. He may be able to place you somewhere on a temporary fill-in basis and continue to do so in the weeks to come.

5—If you were or still are a member of a trade or business association, tell the secretary of the local office to keep you in mind. He may pave the way for you to make a connection.

6—If you held executive positions and feel that you can still meet given requirements, register with the "Forty Plus" club in your community. Get better acquainted with its members, let them know all of your qualifications and let your combined efforts help you find a suitable position.

7—If you are on good terms with your former employer, and there are no reasons why you should not be, talk things over with him. Discuss your needs with former co-workers or associates. It is surprising how often good leads can be uncovered through them.

8—Mention your needs to friends, to your fraternal brothers, to people you know in the commercial or industrial field. Let them be on the "lookout" for you.

9—Arrange to see the heads of the newer and smaller firms in fields with which you are familiar. Stress your knowledge and background to them and offer to give them the benefit of your experience at a reduced rate or on a part-time basis, for the time being.

10—Evaluate your hobbies and leisure time activities as to their marketable values. If you are an expert in a given field or have special aptitudes; if you know how to make, fix or handle certain items; if you are good at sewing, baking, knitting, canning, cooking or planning social gatherings; if animals take to you or if children like to be with you; if you can manage a given business or are good at selling certain items, capitalize on those abilities. Make sure to contact stores or firms within such fields. They will be glad to utilize your skill and pay you for your services.

11—Place carefully worded advertisements in the situation-wanted columns of your local papers and appropriate trade magazines. Be specific in your ad. Emphasize what you can do and why they who might employ you would benefit.

12—Create a job for yourself. If you gained experience in a given field and know it well, there may be "blind spots" or "leaks" in the making or the servicing of the product. And, if you know how to correct or eliminate those trouble spots, your surely have something to sell, something that employers will be anxious to buy.

The twelve ways given to look for and to find a job worked well for others and will be just as helpful to you if you keep this basic thought in mind. Tell your story from the employer's point of view. Stress what he gains and not what you need or want. Back your story with factual proof, with dates, names, places and pertinent details. Then, if there is a job and your age is not an impassable barrier, you will surely have a good chance to get it.

However, because of your age and because you do not have to build for a future, you have to be ready to compromise. You may be asked to work for less money or take orders from someone who does not have your knowledge and experience. You may have to take second and even third choice and "step back" for someone younger than you who has a future to plan for. But none of that should bother you or upset you in any way. Your main interest is to supplement your present income and if the job you get gives it to you, be satisfied.

### How to Get Part-time Work

Your best bet to get full-time work, if you have to have that income, is to find several part-time jobs. For instance, there may be several small young firms or some that are just getting started in fields which you know well. They could use your services but they cannot pay you the money you would ask for a full-time job. But supposing you offered to work for them, a few hours a week, at a fraction of what they would have to pay you ordinarily, they would certainly be interested and eager to avail themselves of your services.

Arrange to work for them a certain number of hours each week. Make the same arrangements with several other firms in the same or in allied fields. Let your fee be small enough to make them eager to employ you on your terms, and before long you will be working as many hours and days a week as you wish.

Here are a few examples:

1—A former pay roll clerk, arbitrarily retired from an industrial plant at age 65, had to supplement his income. He tried vainly to get other employment but his age was against him. He decided to offer a bookkeeping service to small neighborhood merchants at an average fee of ten to twenty dollars a month. Within a year he had enough accounts to use a full-time office girl and an assistant during the income tax periods.

2—A retired schoolteacher who had to use up all of her savings to pay for major surgery had to find a way to supplement her pension. There were no jobs to be had other than selling. Being interested in retarded children and having the place to keep them, she decided to tutor a few at her home. Her charge was low and she had a way with those children. The news spread. Within a year she had to engage another teacher to help her and by the end of the second year her day school for retarded children became a recognized local institution.

3—A mother of five who had no business training and had to work to support herself and her children was exceptionally good in making fancy cookies and devising appetizing tidbits. A friend suggested she approach local clubs and offer to provide her home-baked specialties for their social affairs. People liked her "goodies" and within several months she had enough business to rent a store and start rendering a catering service.

4—A former dress designer, arbitrarily removed from her job because of her age, joined forces with a former drama coach and a cosmetician. They opened a charm school, put on fashion shows and taught women how to dress. It was not too long before they had enough students and enough business to be well satisfied with their efforts.

5—Several retired businessmen with extensive experience in merchandising and public relations, who belonged to the same club, decided to form a business counseling service. They placed appropriate notices in trade publications, got several nice write-ups about their combined business background and soon afterwards began to get calls for their services. Before long they had to extend their services to include marketing, financing and personnel management. By the end of the year they had two branch offices and were profitably occupied most of the time.

These examples were taken at random. Many more could be cited but these should be sufficient to show how a little ingenuity can create a job for the person who is resourceful.

However, if you do not want a steady full-time or part-time job, you could do seasonal work during certain months or during the holiday period. Many of the shops and stores need extra help and you could fill in as a biller, stock clerk, wrapper, checker or an extra sales person. In most cases little experience is needed and most places will train you at their own expense.

If you like to talk with people you may like sales work in such fields as real estate, home furnishings or major electrical appliances where trained people work with you until such time when you feel you can go at it alone.

If you are a woman who does not object to serving food or waiting on tables, you can find part-time work as a waitress or a short order cook during the lunch or dinner hours, even within your own neighborhood or only a short distance away.

If you are a man who likes to putter around a garden or are interested in horticulture, you can find desirable part-time employment in nurseries, garden supply houses or stores which sell patio or garden furniture.

Go back to the lists you prepared, to the inventory you made of your experiences and abilities, of your likes and interests, and deduce from them the jobs you could handle. Set aside the notion that you must follow the work you did before. Be willing to try your hand at something totally different. You may like it better than anything you did before and be happy in doing it.

### How to Start a Business of Your Own

If you have some money and want to start a business of your own, you have to be doubly sure of yourself. You have to know the odds against you and all the risks you face before you invest a single dollar in your proposed venture.

The mortality among small businesses is very high. Among the reasons for failures are: (1) Lack of sufficient knowledge, training or experience. (2) Poor managerial or executive ability. (3) Wrong location. (4) Overstocks of slow-selling items. (5) Overbuying of seasonal merchandise. (6) Lack of working capital. (7) Failure to evaluate changes in uses, trends or conditions. (8) Unwillingness to go through an apprenticeship and learn all the phases of the business. (9) Overconfidence in the ability to meet competition.

(10) Inability to go through the necessary incubation period. (11) Inability to cope with all the cares of a business. (12) The wrong attitudes about shoppers, buyers and demanding customers.

The owner of a small business must be many things in one. He must know what to buy and how to buy, how to sell and how to merchandise slow-moving items, how to manage the business and how to meet contingencies, how to deal with help and how to handle emergencies. Some people are not attuned to it mentally and emotionally and you may be one of them.

You cannot afford to experiment and you must not kid yourself about your abilities and qualifications. Going into a business is risky enough without having to learn at your own expense all the "ins" and "outs" of the business.

Be sure of yourself before you start. Never confuse your years of working in one phase of a business with over-all practical knowledge needed to conduct every phase of such business. You may be a wizard at selling or manufacturing but turn up a "cropper" in trying to handle the buying, merchandising, financing, advertising or personnel details.

The bland assertion that you will learn as you go along may prove most tragic for you. Ask yourself, can you afford to take the chance of losing your investment? Do you know how much business you will have to do to cover your fixed expenses, your variable expenditures and your own living expenses? Have you enough cash to carry you through a complete cycle of sales seasons? How good is the location you selected? What kind of competition will you have to buck? What will you be able to offer to offset the competition? These and dozens of other questions will have to be answered before you invest your precious dollars into the business.

Among the things to do beforehand are:

1—Write to the Small Business Administration, Washington 25, D. C. Ask for the booklets, "So, You're Going Into Business," and "Starting a Business of Your Own." Or, ask for details about the particular business in which you are interested.

2—Discuss your proposed entry into the business with the manager of your own bank or with the officials of the bank in the community where you intend to operate. They may have records on file and up-to-date findings on business of a similar nature as compiled for bank loan officers and for credit organizations.

3—Check with the trade and the business associations in the area. If there are no local offices, discuss your plans with jobbers, wholesalers, salesmen and retailers in that field. Do not depend upon the opinion of one salesman or one jobber but talk to several of them. Ask them to be frank with you and tell you if the business or the location or the chances are not in your favor.

4—If it is possible, go to work for someone in that line of business, in a location or in a situation similar to the one you will have to meet. Offer to work for a ridiculous wage or for no payment. Offer to work during the busy season if you cannot get in at any other time, and postpone your own entry into that field until you learn at firsthand all the things you need to know.

If, on the other hand, you have had no special business experience and still want to work at something for yourself, there are many types of individualized or personalized service-type businesses which you can enter. For instance, you can open a dry cleaning agency, an automatic laundry, a doughnut store worked under a franchise, a cigar stand in an office building or get into a small vending route. However, be sure to check and double-check every franchise with the aid of your attorney and your banker before you pay out money for some get-rich-quick scheme.

Some small service-type business can be worked from your home—a typing or mailing service, a fix-it shop, a clearing house for baby sitters, a phone answering service or a credit check service. As a matter of fact, some of the part-time jobs mentioned earlier in this chapter could very well be started and conducted, with little capital, from your home.

### How to Develop Other Sources of Income

To derive an income from other sources you have to put your money to work. This calls for a reinvestment of capital funds and you should consider all angles and possibilities very carefully before you sell your blue chip stocks or withdraw your savings. Make doubly sure that your contemplated investment does not involve risks too big and perhaps even tragic for you.

Among the things you can do are:

1—If your present home is too large for your needs and the market for selling is favorable, you might sell your house and use the proceeds to buy residential or commercial property.

2—If existing zoning permits it or if there has been a rezoning of properties in your locality, you may be able to convert a large house into multiple units or into offices. This may call for remodeling and may or may not be advisable. Be sure to check those possibilities carefully and thoroughly, not only with two or three general contractors, but also with your bank and your attorney before the conversion. Be sure of your ground before you take on the extra obligations and before you assume mortgages and other payments which might endanger your original investment.

3—If you have a big house and do not want to convert it into multiple units of offices, you could consider its possible use as a guest house, with or without meals. Or, you could rent rooms to mothers with preschool children who need day care. Or, you could take in older people and with the aid of a practical nurse serve the needs of several aged persons in your community.

4—If your lot is big enough or deep enough you could build income units in the rear. Or, if it is worth the costs involved, you could have the old house removed and build multiple units, with the idea of occupying one and managing the others.

5—If you have a house and a little extra cash besides, it might pay you to trade upwards for some income producing property that will give you a home and the desired income.

6—If you want to work at something and have some money to invest, you may find it desirable to buy an interest in a going business and by working in it have a job, an extra income and a better return on your money. However, you have to be very careful and not get into anything without thorough investigation. Be sure to check with your banker, your attorney, your Better Business Bureau, the suppliers, the customers, and others who know something about the proposed associate and his past record.

It is very easy to find people anxious to sell you an interest in their business who paint glorious pictures of returns. Some of your immediate relatives may also wish to go into a partnership with you and promise you exceptional profits if you provide the necessary cash. But be sure to check all offers and promises very carefully and do not allow emotion or sentiment to sway you.

7—If you have certain skills and can teach them to others, you may do well by starting a small instruction class. You could go at it alone, from your home, or take in someone with you, someone to carry the load and handle the tiring details. But here, too, make sure of your ground and especially of the person you take in as your associate.

Here are several examples of such simple projects:

A. Mary Brown had a large single house and was interested in playing bridge. She started a bridge and canasta club. She supplies lunches at one dollar per person, charges a dollar each for every table used and takes in enough cash each week to provide her with the extra income desired.

B. Alice Smith had an eight-room house with a large patio, spacious yard and barbecue. She started renting out the rooms for afternoon and evening meetings at five dollars each, and $7.50 each for parties and barbecues in her back yard. Her house is well located and she has a waiting list for small groups who want to meet in her home.

C. Abner Johnson, a retired cabinet maker, attended an auction for curiosity's sake and bought woodworking equipment at a bargain. He converted his double garage into a workshop and began teaching his grandchildren simplified cabinet making. They spread the word and soon the parents of other children began asking him to teach their children. The neighborhood PTA, the school board and the civic juvenile authority liked the idea and urged Abner to extend his services. He is now kept busy at his shop five days a week, doing what he likes to do and making money at it.

D. Leslie Warner was handy with the needle and extremely good at fixing clothes. She approached two neighborhood cleaners and offered to do minor tailoring and alteration jobs at a low price. They liked the idea and so did their customers. Before long she had a nice following and was earning more than enough in extra money to meet her needs.

E. George Baxter, familiar with the principles of electricity, with time on his hands, began fixing small electrical appliances for members of his family and his immediate neighbors. Seemingly useless irons, toasters, mixers, fans, table and floor lamps, heaters and vacuum cleaners became as good as new under his hands. Strangers began asking him to fix things for them. He had to move from the house into the garage and from the garage into a store. Soon afterwards he became the acknowledged "Mr. Fix-it" for the entire area, at a profit to himself and to others.

F. Grace Lawson was fond of folk dancing. She learned the caller's patter and for the fun of it undertook to conduct several folk-dancing parties for her club and her church sisterhood. She was good at "calling" and was asked to officiate at several other similar affairs. She was also asked to give a few private lessons. Before long she found herself devoting several hours a week to teaching. Then someone suggested she arrange a public folk dance on Saturday nights at a small fee per person. She took it up and soon afterwards was earning enough extra money to meet her needs.

These examples demonstrate how something you know or like to do can be utilized to bring financial returns. So— check into your skills or hobbies carefully and ascertain which one can be put to work to bring you an extra income.

## How to Get Old Age or Social Security Benefits

If you are sick or disabled, if you have to have an additional income and cannot work, you may be able to get financial assistance from one of these sources:

1—If you are an American citizen, have been a resident of the same state and county for the required period of time, and if you have no children to support you or any negotiable assets you may be entitled to "Old Age Assistance" as provided for by your state. The requirements and the amounts payable are not the same in all states, but whatever the provisions are you have to apply at the nearest social service agency or at the Bureau of Public Assistance. In many instances help is provided even when one does not ordinarily qualify for assistance.

In the state of California, as a citizen and as a resident of the state for five years or more, you can apply to the local office of the Bureau of Public Assistance, to the county or state social welfare agencies or to the Senior Citizen's Center which will help you get the financial and medical aid you need.

Such assistance will be given to you even if your family or children could support you. You will be asked to fill out certain forms and your children will be required to submit financial statements. However, under the statutes of responsibility for the support of elderly parents, a married daughter cannot be held liable or made to contribute. A son is obliged to help but only in proportion to his financial ability and his net income as shown by his financial statement and his current federal and state income tax returns.

The maximum old age assistance to a single person in California was $106.00 a month at the time this survey was made. It included free medical care and hospitalization in any county hospital. There were additional benefits and services for the blind, the disabled, the handicapped and the mentally disturbed who were placed in institutions.

If you do not qualify for old age assistance and cannot pay for the medical or mental service needed, there are various groups and associations which may help you. Among them are the American Cancer Society, the Association for Mental Health, the Heart Foundation, the County Medical Association, the Diabetes Society, the Bureau of Mental Hygiene, the National Association for the Prevention of Blindness, the Tuberculosis and Health Association, the Asthmatic Help Society, the free clinics at various hospital, the city or county health department, the civic charity groups and the welfare societies maintained by churches, synagogues and fraternal orders.

2—If you are a retiree from a union job, belong to a given church affiliate or are a member in good standing of a fraternal order, you may be entitled to old age and sickness benefits as provided by the group under its by-laws and its constitution. Such help may be given to you in addition to whatever assistance you get from your city, county or state. Many of the unions, churches and fraternal orders maintain homes for the aged, and if need be, will place you in the home best suited to your needs. And, if you have dependents, will make provisions to care for them.

3—If you are a veteran or the wife of a veteran, the nearest post, auxiliary or unit of the American Legion and the Veterans of Foreign Wars will be glad to advise you and to assist you to get aid from the nearest Veterans Administration office. They will do all they can to intercede for you and secure the medical and hospitalization care you need, especially if yours is a borderline case and is not considered a direct service connected disability.

You may be entitled to Social Security benefits under the amendments adopted in 1960 and the rulings of 1961. You may be eligible even if you never worked under Social Security coverage or if, as a worker, you were disabled before or after your 50th birthday, some time ago.

Under the new provisions you would be entitled to benefits if you were the dependent of a disabled or deceased worker who still has a wife and children under eighteen drawing monthly benefits. You would be eligible now, even though your application was turned down at any time prior to 1961. And such payments would be retroactive for twelve months immediately preceding your new application.

The rulings of 1961 had these important changes:

A. If you are disabled and it happened before or after your 50th birthday, you may qualify for Social Security disability benefits now, if you were under coverage for a minimum of five years out of the last ten years prior to your disability and providing your disability prevents you from "engaging in any substantial gainful activity."

In other words, your disability must be of such mental or physical nature which will show up in medical tests or examinations. It must be at least six months old and be expected to continue indefinitely. The extent of benefits payable to you will be determined not only by your disabled physical or mental condition, but it will also be evaluated in the light of your age, work record, training, knowledge and needed rehabilitation.

B. As the aged father or mother of a disabled Social Security beneficiary who carried you as his dependent, you are eligible for monthly benefits now, even though you were turned down at any time previously.

C. As the dependent parent of a deceased worker you are eligible for benefits, even if his wife and children under 18 have been getting their survivor benefits for a long time.

D. If you are the widow of a worker who died before 1940, you may be eligible for monthly payments at this time.

E. Under the 1961 rulings you may earn up to $1,200.00 a year until you reach your 72nd birthday without losing any part of your Social Security benefits. If you earn more, you lose at the rate of one dollar for every two earned between $1,200.00 and $1,700.00, and one dollar for each dollar earned over $1,700.00. These losses apply only to wages received as a regular employee of a given company and do not apply to income from pensions, annuities, dividends, royalties, rents or returns from investments, no matter how much the total is for any calendar year. The losses in benefits are applicable only until you reach your 72nd birthday, after which no matter how much you earn in wages you still receive your full retirement benefits.

Several important liberalizations were made since and others are still pending. Among them are:

1—Earlier Retirement Privileges. A man, if he so desires, can retire at age 62. His benefits would be 80% of the amount due him if his earnings had remained the same and if he had waited until age 65. And he needs only thirteen quarters, $3\frac{1}{4}$ years, under Social Security coverage, to qualify.

2—Lower Age for Beneficiaries. The age for paying benefits to dependent husbands or widowers of women workers was also lowered from age 65 to age 62.

3—Higher Benefits. The minimum amount now payable

to those over 65 to their dependents or survivors is $40.00 a month. And payments to two survivors were increased to $60.00 a month.

4—Increased Widow Benefits. Payments to widows were increased approximately 10%. Under the new rulings she gets 82½% of what her husband received or would have received had he lived.

5—Reduction in Work Credits. An applicant needs as little as six quarters, 1½ years, of work under Social Security coverage, to qualify for his retirement benefits and get at least $40.00 a month.

6—Easier Survivor Requirements. The survivor of a worker who died after June 1954, who was not eligible under previous limitations, may be entitled to benefits under the new rulings.

7—More Time for Claims. Applicants with long-time disabilities who delayed completing necessary claims or were denied benefits because of the time lapse have additional extensions to present new claims.

## Increased Medical Aid

Under the Kerr-Mills Medical Plan for the Aged, passed by Congress in 1960, you are entitled to financial aid to meet all or part of your medical expenses. The aid is based upon your ability to pay and upon the MAA, the Medical Assistance for the Aged, as adopted by your state to match Federal funds.

In California for instance, if you are on the OAS, the Old Age Assistance rolls, you get free medical, surgical and hospital services. You also get free glasses, dental services and prescribed drugs. But your state may have different regulations.

If you are under Social Security benefits and have other incomes but are still in the low-income bracket, you pay what you can and your state pays the difference. For instance, if your total income averages $2,000 a year and you have a large medical bill to pay, you can ask your local MAA office or the Welfare Aid Agency to help you. That office will investigate your request and if it is approved, will authorize full or part payment of the costs.

The degree of help given will be governed by the established "Standard of Need" in your state and the extent of such aid will be based upon the provisions for its aged citizens, because although the Federal government will contribute from 50 to 80 per cent of the funds needed, each state will have its own rulings and standards.

For instance, one state will make full allowance for glasses and dentures but another will not. One state will honor the bills tendered only by members of the American Medical Association while another will also pay for services rendered to an aged person by a chiropractor, an osteopath or a Christian Science practitioner.

Whatever be the standards and allowances set by your state and the Social Security benefits which were or were not given to you, be sure to check your present eligibility. Make inquiries at the nearest Social Security office, at your social welfare agency or at the senior citizen service center, because you may be entitled to services denied to you only a few months back.

In connection with your present retirement income, if you do or do not supplement it with part-time or full-time work, you may have to pay an income tax, especially since the Mill Bill, signed by the President on October 24, 1962, became the law of the land.

If an accountant or an income tax man prepares your returns you need not concern yourself with the new Federal Income Tax Rules and Regulations, but if you prepare your returns or if you wish to know its newest provisions you can get the information by writing to the Superintendent of Documents, Washington 25, D. C., and ask for the booklet "Your Federal Income Tax." The cost is forty cents. Or, you can buy a new booklet written especially for senior adults for one dollar. It is published by the Interstate Printing Co., Danville, Ill., and its title is "Federal Taxes on Benefits from Your Retirement Income."

Under the provisions of the Mill Bill there is a larger tax credit available to you. The maximum allowance is now $304.80 as against $240.00 in 1961. It exempts all Social Security and Railroad Retirement benefits from Federal taxation and provides other exemptions for retired persons.

Follow through on some of the ways suggested to supplement your income and on how to get needed aid from accredited sources in your community. Check into every means to add to your income and then you will surely add joy and happiness to your golden years.

# CHAPTER ELEVEN

# How to Benefit by Group Dynamics

There was a time in your life, before you retired, when your "work" time and your "play" time, figuratively speaking, were worlds apart.

In the usual meaning of the word, your "work" was your job, your occupation or profession, the things you had to do each day, whether or not you liked it, to earn your livelihood. Your "play" was what you wanted or enjoyed doing but you could do it only during your leisure hours.

But nowadays, unless you have to work to supplement your income, you can combine your "work time" and your "play time" into one or several recreational activities to suit your desire. What is more, you can join others to share your common interests, to combine your efforts, to coordinate your various activities and thus benefit by the positive aspects of group dynamics.

But, you might ask, what is group dynamics, or what is dynamics?

Dynamics is the science that deals with the laws of force in their relation to matter, at rest or in motion, and with the effects of such laws as expressed in time, space, action and reaction.

Nearly three hundred years ago Sir Isaac Newton gave us these three basic laws of force:

1—That any given body remains in a state of rest or in a uniform motion along a straight line, unless its is compelled by another force to change its state.

2—That a change in rate or the direction of motion is in proportion to the force employed and it occurs along a straight line in which such force acts.

3—That as a result of every action there is an equal, constant, compensating resistance or reaction.

A dynamic force can be negative or positive, constructive or destructive in its action. Fill a container with detonating explosive elements and use the force of propulsion to hurl the container through space at terrific speed to strike some opposing object and you will have a bomb or a bullet to shatter or to kill. Use the same dynamic force of propulsion and explosion to send a piston up and down a cylinder block to put various gears into motion and you will have a motor to propel an automobile or to do other useful tasks for you.

The science of dynamics has many branches. There is mechano-dynamics, dealing with static energy in solids under the action of force and with kinetic energy that deals with force producing action in solid bodies. There are gas dynamics, fluid dynamics, flight-dynamics and thermodynamics. There is aerodynamics which concerns itself with the effects of mechanical forces in their relation to air and gases on the sonic, subsonic and supersonic levels.

There is nuclei-dynamics dealing with molecules and atoms in action; psycho-physic dynamics which is the study of action and response to various physical and mental stimuli; and group dynamics. It deals with the effects of human contact and influences, where a number of individuals work as a group or a team, where different people combine efforts, interests, forces and activities to maintain or attain certain desired objectives.

The impact of dynamic action is in the effects of directed motion and that is the basis of all animate and inanimate life. Without motion and compensating reaction, without pull and resistance, without attraction and repulsion, nothing could exist. You and everything solid within you and around you would explode instantly if the molecular energy stored within each solid were to be released and if the existing molecular formations were forced to change their present pre-established and predetermined motion within their respective peripheries.

Each molecular motion remains constant so long as the existing order, rate or frequency of motion is not subjected to a change. For instance, water will retain its fluidity so long as no changes in basic content or temperature are introduced. But let the factor of cold or heat be introduced and you will have ice or steam. Let new chemicals be added to the water and you will have something entirely new and different.

This great, big, wonderful world of ours would immediately fall apart if its orbit around the sun, its rate of speed in the orbit, its gravitational pull or atmospheric density were to undergo a change. This book and its pages would disintegrate in a moment if it were not for the molecular motion and structure involved in maintaining them in their present state.

Everything in you and about you is in constant motion. For instance, under normal conditions the valves of your heart open and close at the rate of seventy-two times a minute or more than one hundred thousand times a day. Should this con-

stancy in rhythmic order change in any way you would have
a heart ailment and should your heart stop beating for frac-
tions of a minute you would die.

As a pump, your heart circulates the five to six quarts
of blood in your veins almost two thousand times a day and
in so doing your blood covers a route from sixty thousand to
one hundred thousand miles during every twenty-four hours.
Should a blood clot form anywhere along this long route to
interfere in any way with the normal flow of blood, gangrene
will set in and, unless corrected quickly, will lead to your
death.

Everything that you see, hear, feel, taste, smell, know,
recall or experience comes to you through a form of motion;
motion that is translated through similar electrical charges
or impulses. The difference is only in the rate or number,
in the size or the frequency of those charges. The selection,
identification and the interpretation is made by various sections of your brain.

Each section is attuned to certain stimuli. Once inter-
cepted it is translated in the light of your knowledge and past
contacts or experiences. They, in turn, induce the response.
But, curiously enough, your responses are not always the
same, because your mood or your feeling, the place or the
circumstance, the people or some new development may
change your interpretation and evoke an entirely different
response.

Neurologists have learned within recent years how to
identify, segregate, amplify or nullify various response-pro-
ducing areas in the brain. Hence, when your physical or
mental health calls for it, surgeons can perform lobotomies
and thereby deaden certain portions of your brain to arrest
or preclude the sensory responses harmful to your well-being.

Now, you might ask what relation is there between response and group dynamics? The answer is predicated upon you, as the transmitter, recorder and interpreter. Figuratively speaking, nothing can reach you or touch you unless it comes through your own senses. They, in turn, are governed by the sum total of your knowledge, background, beliefs, opinions, convictions and even prejudices. You live in a little world all your own where the things that impinge upon it are measured by your feelings and emotions.

You follow a set orbit, surrounded by your fears, worries, anxieties, successes and disappointments. The only time when the orbit changes is when you widen your horizons, enlarge your concepts, make new contacts and acquire new interests. Your orbit is further enlarged when you join others in a mutual effort to gain a certain objective.

Then you reach out into other little worlds such as yours and come under the gravitational attraction of other personalities, in a merger of interests and activities that remove you temporarily from the narrowed limits of your preoccupation with your own personality. Then you become part of a team with all of you working together in a friendly, cooperative spirit, and the force of group dynamics is now being used in your favor. However, to derive the full benefits of such dynamic forces, certain personal adjustments are required of you.

You have to subordinate personal preferences, set aside preconceived notions, make allowances for differences in character and background, cultivate a cooperative attitude, assume your share of the responsibilities, and work in unison with the rest to reach the objectives of the group.

These are some of the ways to benefit by the positive aspects of group dynamics:

THERE'S GOLD IN YOUR GOLDEN AGE

1—Join a group, if you do not already belong to one, where some of their activities interest you or where you can cultivate an interest in the things they are doing. You may be able to contribute very little in actual work or in experience but your readiness to take part and your willingness to follow the lead of others will be in your favor and will enable you to benefit by the group dynamics.

2—Start a new project with a group to which you belong that will deal with a given need that appeals to you and that can be made interesting to the rest. It might be in the field of social service, to work with retarded children, to prevent juvenile delinquency, to assist the blind or the handicapped, to help rehabilitate the mentally sick or disabled veterans. The value to you will be in the merger of interests, in the fusing of personalities, in the common effort to help those in need, and in so doing your own personal cares and difficulties will be minimized.

Your project could be a "Big Brother" or "Big Sister" plan, or an interracial committee to work with the problems of the minorities in your town. It could be the idea of fostering closer cooperation between religious groups, to promote better understanding between parents and children, or to bring together men and women in all walks of life in communal undertakings.

And, should members of an established group be unwilling to work with you, there will be others eager to cooperate when you ask them. At times it is only necessary to talk things over with several key people, such as the pastor or preacher of your church, the rabbi of your congregation, the officials of a civic organization, the executive director of a related social agency, the members of your union or trade association, the city editor of your local paper, the members of your

Golden Age club, the workers at your nearest community center or some of your immediate neighbors. You need only a handful of people to get things started.

3—Propose to a carefully selected number of people the idea to share skills, knowledge and ability, one with the other. It could be done in the forms of talks, classes or discussions, and at the beginning the meetings could be held at the homes of the various participants. The plan would be to have each person undertake to tell or teach others how to do something he knows well. It could be playing bridge, tooling leather, knitting garments, playing a musical instrument, learning another language or public speaking. It holds tremendous possibilities for all concerned and when properly handled could become a most interesting and enlightening way to add joys and pleasures to everyday living.

Be willing to learn. Keep your mind open and welcome the opportunity to try your hand at something new and different. You have no way of telling what will or will not appeal to you in the long run. You have many untapped abilities which never came to light. Give them the chance to break through.

Expose yourself to the gravitational pull of other personalities, to the ideas of people you meet, to the views they hold and the interests they follow. This may call for a few changes in your habits, in some of your tastes and established routines, but those things may be just what you need to awaken your "bump of curiosity," to arouse your creative urges and uncover your hidden talents.

You will get nowhere by "sitting it out alone," by demanding that others follow your lead or you will not play, by being arbitrary or dictatorial. You will get nowhere by living only with yourself, by dwelling only upon your selfish interests, by being preoccupied with your own little world, by coddling yourself or by looking for shoulders upon which to cry.

Do not expect people to cater to you, to be attentive and sympathetic just because you want it that way. It is not enough to join a group or give lip service to some of its activities and expect to be complimented for it. You have to be willing to work, to get into the spirit of things, to give of yourself, to be amiable and cooperative.

It is the attitude you take and the interest you display. It is the responsibility you assume and the willingness you show. It is the way you go about working with the people you joined in a common objective. It is your acceptance of conditions which may not be to your liking. It is your reaction and behavior in the face of pressure or criticism. It is the measure of your loyalty and sincerity of purpose. It is the impression others get of your stability and integrity of character. It is your ability to bring out the potentialities of others. It is the use you make of your good points and attributes. All of these things determine your value to yourself as well as to others and how much good you will derive from group dynamics.

Group dynamics can become a powerful force in your life when you give it the chance to work in your favor. Let it bring color, value, meaning and beauty into your life. Then you will be welcome wherever you go and good at whatever you do. Then you will remain alert in mind and young at heart as you add more calendar years to your beautiful golden age.

CHAPTER TWELVE

# How to Find Suitable Housing

Whatever else you do, unless you are entirely dependent upon others, try to retain your home or maintain your own living quarters.

Your children or grandchildren, your son-in-law or daughter-in-law may be sincere in the desire to have you live with them but you would be better off in many ways not to succumb to the temptation and give up your home. The differences in age, in habits, in mode of behavior and in ways of living may not be too noticeable at first, but as you continue to live together constant irritations and dissatisfactions will develop. The differences will engender quarrels, foster misunderstandings, build up resentments and eventually turn into open animosities.

A house or an apartment or just a room apart from your children, even if you have a poor income and have to make sacrifices in other ways, will more than repay you in freedom of action and in peace of mind. It matters not how small, simple or unpretentious those living quarters might be, they will become your sanctuary, your haven of rest and peace.

The retention of your private living quarters will give you many important advantages. Among them are:

1—You will retain your total entity and dignity as an individual and not become that "old man" or the "old woman" in someone else's house.

2—You will not be beholden to the wishes or the opinions of a son, a daughter or a grandchild who may have all the good intentions in the world and yet meddle with your daily life.

3—You will be free to come and go as you please, eat what you want and when you want, go to sleep or sit up late to suit yourself and do whatever you feel like doing without having to explain or to justify yourself to someone who may criticize or censure you.

4—You will be able to engage in any activity desired, at home or elsewhere, invite and entertain the people you like in any way to suit you, without questioning or recriminations from your children.

5—You will avoid becoming involved in family situations, in squabbles or misunderstandings where you may be forced to take sides and aggravate matters.

6—You will retain your self-respect and your precious independence, especially if the ways and the habits of the younger generation grate on you or interfere with your habitual behavior.

7—You will have a better chance to find satisfaction and happiness within the framework of your age and your limitations away from the questioning or disapproving eyes of your family.

This does not imply that you should estrange yourself from your children. On the contrary, be devoted to them. Do all you can for them. See them as often as you find it desirable, but let those visits be on a temporary basis. In other words, retain your private living quarters so as to be free to lead your own life.

Of course, if you are financially secure you need give little thought to housing accommodations. You can change your residences from season to season, from place to place, and even from one country to another to suit your whims and fancies. You can have your choice of the best in hotels and in apartments, the finest in beach or mountain resorts or the most exclusive clubhouses, geared to provide all the comforts, conveniences and luxuries that money can buy.

Specially built places catering to the retired rich person and giving him every type of service and attention desired is nothing new. They are to be found in every city and resort center in the world. But apartments built especially for older people, where each tenant owns his living quarters, is a fairly new development on the American scene. A number of such cooperative apartment houses under a central management control have been built in many parts of the country.

One of those specially constructed cooperative apartment houses on the West Coast was described in detail in a featured article titled "No Housing Worry Here," in the October 24, 1959 issue of the *Saturday Evening Post*. It is a seven million dollar twenty-two acre project known as the Willamette Manor near Portland, Oregon.

It is a residential type hotel where six hundred guests, or "founders" as they are called, purchased their respective living quarters in the hotel at prices varying from $7,500.00 to $20,000.00, based upon the size, location and number of rooms occupied. This purchase relieved the "founder" of all the costs, cares and responsibilities of individual home care and maintenance.

The Willamette Manor, interdenominational in character, caters to people past fifty years of age who are in good health, who meet the requirements, who can afford to make the original investment and pay afterwards a flat rate of one hundred dollars a month for food and room service. This $100.00 a month charge provides each resident with his choice of food, served privately or in dining rooms, and with all the services and facilities of a better class American Plan hotel.

In addition, there are planned sport and recreational activities, educational programs, a well-stocked library and specially built shops for those who wish to follow a given mechanical or artistic hobby. There is also a hospital where, with the exception of major surgery, a complete medical service is provided for every resident, free of charge.

The Willamette Manor also maintains infirmary wings for the founders who need continuous medical care or hospitalization. The costs for such services are fixed in advance, payable on a monthly basis, and each resident can shift from one service to another as and when the need arises.

Residents are free of any form of regimentation. They can come and go as they wish and be active or inactive in any of the activities made available to all. Self-regulating committees selected by the residents, with the advice of professionals on the regular staff of the manor, arrange card and birthday parties, musicales, lectures, discussions, tournaments, desirable excursions and other group events for those who wish to participate. The rest can keep to themselves or follow their particular interests, singly or in company with others. Residents also have the right to sell their apartments back to the management, subject to certain restrictions and provisions.

In contrast to the Willamette type of cooperative residential units there are many low-rent housing projects built by a county or a state for its elderly citizens under the 1956 Housing Act.

One of them is the Cedar Apartments project at Cleveland, Ohio, with an average rental of thirty dollars a month. The fourteen-story buildings have nonskid floors, modern kitchen aids, safety bars in the bathrooms, service elevators and many other safety features. The ground floors have various hobby shops, lounges and meeting rooms. In addition, there are planned day and evening programs and activities adapted to the interests and the abilities of the residents so as to keep their hands and their minds busy.

The Cleveland project removed many elderly people from nursing homes and hospitals. It is saving the state of Ohio thousands of dollars a day. Many an ailing person who was bedridden or mentally disturbed, who needed medical care and costly around-the-clock nursing services, suddenly found himself well enough and able enough to take care of himself. Once again he became a self-respecting member of his community, pleased with his new status as an independent home keeper and eager to prove to all that he can take better care of himself.

Another project of this type is in Asbury Park, New Jersey. It is a seven-story, fifty-unit apartment. The one and two-bedroom apartments rent for $35.00 and $45.00 a month. All units have many safety features and the ground floor has a lounge, hobby shops and meeting halls. Recreational facilities are also provided outside of the building. The demand was so large that several other similar buildings were started almost immediately around New Jersey and New York City.

Other specially built housing units for the elderly, to

mention only a few of them, are: the Rouge Valley Manor, Medford, Ore.; the Waltham, Mass. project; the White Sands, La Jolla, Calif.; the Royal Oaks Manor, Duarte, Calif.; and the Yerba Buena Annex, San Francisco, Calif.

A different type of low-rent housing project, a whole community for older people, in the planning stage at the time this survey was made, is the Senior Citizens Village, Fresno, Calif. It is sponsored by George McLain and the California Institute of Social Welfare and could serve as a model for other communities.

The plans call for eighty ranch-type, one-story buildings, a total of 556 units. They are to be equipped with stoves, refrigerators, air conditioners and laundry rooms. The buildings would be grouped around a large diversified shopping area and a big community center. There will be hobby shops, a cafeteria, a movie house, "meals on wheels" services, medical offices, an infirmary and several places of worship.

With the amendments in the 1959 FHA Housing Regulations, where private interests are backed financially to build homes and apartments for the elderly, many of such projects were undertaken in different parts of the country. Among them at the time this survey was made, and the list is not complete, were:

Youngtown, a community of one thousand single homes built especially for elderly people, sixteen miles from Phoenix, Ariz. The prices range from $7,500.00 to $12,000.00 each. The community has an extensive shopping area, churches, a theater, a community center and planned recreational activities for those who want to follow them.

Another similar community in Arizona, privately developed, is Wickenberg West, 54 miles from Phoenix. Still another on the outskirts of Phoenix is Sun City. Single homes there sell from $8,500.00 to $14,500.00. Or, if preferred, for the sum of $8,000 to $10,000 a person can get clear title to a cooperative care-free, mortgage-free apartment. Sun City has a communal swimming pool, a golf course, hobby shops, sewing rooms, meeting halls, an agricultural project and a large shopping center which also has extensive medical care facilities.

Among the developments in Pennsylvania is the York House in Philadelphia. The rent for those furnished apartments varies from $175.00 to $280.00 a month. This includes meals, maid service, medical care and various recreational facilities. The demand for the apartments was so great that several additional buildings were started shortly afterwards in Philadelphia and in other parts of the country.

Florida has several notable retirement villages such as Melbourne near Miami, Fort Pearce Beach near Palm Beach, and Salhaven at Jupiter. Washington State boasts of Ryderwood. It is located at the foothills of western Washington, surrounded on three sides by forested hills and has its own lake stocked with mountain trout. The 183 homes in the development are sold on long-term mortgages with payments as low as $20.00 a month.

One of the California developers came up with a new idea in retirement villages. The picturesque titles are Suntown-by-the-Sea, Suntown-in-the-Desert, Suntown-in-the-Mountains, and Suntown-in-the-Tropics. Each active Suntown member is given the right to spend part of the time each year in any one of the four locations. The desert retreat is in Cathedral City near Palm Springs, the sea location is at Cardiff near San Diego, the mountain homes are at a three-thousand elevation and the tropical village is in Hawaii. Thus, the Suntowners

can go to the sea, the desert, the mountains or the tropics to
suit their fancy to take advantage of the seasons in the year.

Another California development which was still on the
planning boards at the time the survey was made is the Rossmoor Leisure World, being built near Seal Beach. It covers
540 acres, consists of 6,750 apartments and offers to people
over 52 years of age carefree housing, planned social and
recreational activities and hobby-shop facilities. The purchase
price of an apartment averages $10,000 each and the monthly
payments after a minimum $500.00 down is less than
$100.00 a month, with ownership of such place vested in the
buyer and passed on to his heirs or his estate. Rossmoor
claims to be the first cooperative project to maintain a staff
of doctors, nurses and pharmacists, to provide a complete
drug and medical service to its residents, for a flat extra
charge of less than $50.00 a month.

Two other new developments in California are the 1,800
home and apartment project at Palm City, and the six-thou-
sand-acre project at Stockdale.

One of the most ambitious projects to provide homes for
its elderly members is the one planned by seven major labor
unions under the intriguing title of "Four Freedom Homes."
The plans call for specially built retirement units in 42
major centers at a total cost of over five hundred million dollars. At the time this survey was made, plans were already
completed for five-million dollar units to be built at Seattle,
Detroit and Miami Beach.

The swing toward building retirement projects is steadily
going upward. They vary from many-storied buildings put
in the midst of heavily populated metropolitan centers to
special one-story garden-type villages with their own shopping centers, community buildings and other conveniences.

All have specially built features for the safety and the convenience of the occupants, such as nonskid floors, hand-bars in the bathroom, low easy-to-reach cabinets, ramps instead of stairs, modern kitchen helps and convenient electrical outlets. The communal type projects have main dining rooms, homemaker services, hot meals on wheels, grocery deliveries, daily medical checkups and a visiting nurse service for those in need.

If you prefer to buy or build a home of your own, liberal terms on building and financing are now available to you under Section 203 of the 1956 National Housing Act and the provisions of the FHA Mortgage Insurance plan. You can borrow up to $20,000.00 for a single family dwelling at $5\frac{1}{4}\%$ and a mortgage insurance premium from $\frac{1}{2}\%$ to $1\%$ annually. You need no down payment. The only requirements are that you have an income sufficient enough to repay the down payment, to make the regular monthly payments as determined by your mortgage, to support your family and to maintain the property.

On the other hand, if you prefer to live in a home which caters to certain groups, religious affiliations or other prerequisites, your choice will be determined by one or more of these factors:

1—The amount of cash, personal assets and other sources of revenue that you have with which to pay the required entrance fees and other costs of a given home.

2—The amount of cash down and the necessary monthly fees which your children or someone else can pay for you so as to enable you to become a resident of the home you selected.

3—The extent of the old-age assistance which your state

provides for indigent citizens which may restrict you to a home willing to accept you on that basis.

4—The impairments you have and the state of your physical and mental condition which may force you to look for a home where the needed services and the medical care are provided for the residents.

5—Your religious beliefs, habits, leanings or particular preferences which may influence you to select one home against another.

6—Your membership in a union or an association, a fraternal order or a church affiliation, and the facilities which they have for elderly people.

This applies only where the choice is up to you. Otherwise you have to go wherever you are placed, whether or not such is to your liking.

In the matter of churches, nearly every denomination has homes for the aged. Some of them cater only to members of their own church. Others accept applicants of different faiths and base their selection on the type and the character of the individual rather than upon his religious precepts.

For instance, the Disciples of Christ churches maintain homes for their aged members who need medical care and cannot pay for it. Their entrance fee is only $100.00 and the applicant need only turn over to the home whatever old-age assistance or other income he might have.

The homes are located in many parts of the country and new homes are added as rapidly as funds are accumulated. There are homes in San Gabriel, Calif.; in Jacksonville, Fla.; in Jacksonville, Ill.; in Des Moines, Iowa; in Marion, Ind.; in Columbia, Mo.; in Beavertown, Ore., and in Dallas, Texas.

The Episcopalians had seventy-four homes at the time this survey was made and new ones were added since. Their entrance fees average $500.00 per entrant plus whatever income and other assets he might have. Excellent care is provided for all the residents and every effort is made to add ease and comfort to their lives.

The United Churches of Christ, consisting of the Congregational, Evangelical and Reformed Christian churches, had forty-three homes for the aged at the time this survey was made, with ten more in the initial construction stage.

Among their outstanding developments where every modern comfort, service and convenience are provided for those who can pay for it are the luxurious apartment hotels operated under the sponsorship of Dr. J. W. Fifield of the First Congregational Church of Los Angeles, Calif. They are the Fifield Manor, the Fifield Wilshire and the Fifield Pasadena.

The annual rental is $15.00 per square foot of space plus a monthly charge of $180.00 for meals and services. A resident can also purchase a life contract ranging from $5,000.00 to $25,000.00 depending upon the applicant's age, sex, health and life expectancy.

Another notable Congregational home for the elderly in California is the Pilgrim Place in Claremont. Out of the 156 individual homes there at the time this survey was made, one third of those homes were on the Life Lease plan. The residents paid for the building of the homes and bequeathed them to the church but continue to live there, rent free, during their lifetime.

The Lutherans had 136 homes when this survey was made. Costs to residents ranged from $80.00 to $135.00 a month for room, meals and required medical services. The

Southern Baptists had 14 homes with several additional homes under construction. The Roman Catholics had 314 homes and were constantly building other homes while improving facilities and services in the homes already built. The Jews had 80 homes and were continually adding to existing facilities. In each group the entrance requirements were adjusted to the financial means of the applicant and in a number of homes only the poor and the destitue are eligible.

The Methodists had 104 homes and forty-eight more in the process of being started or completed when this survey was made. More than one half of the existing homes have special facilities for the chronically ill. Entrance is on an individual nondenominational basis. Former teachers, ministers, doctors, missionaries and professional men and women are welcomed.

One of their outstanding developments is the Pacific Homes in California. The parent home is in Los Angeles and has room for 450 residents. The other homes are the Claremont in Claremont, and the Casa de Manana in La Jolla. The entrance fees are based upon age, sex and life expectancy, ranging from $8,000.00 to $18,000.00 for each applicant.

The Presbyterians had 75 homes at the time the check was made and several more were under construction. Notable among their homes is Westminster Gardens in Duarte, Calif., and the Pynmyre at Cooperstown, N. Y. These two homes are maintained mostly for retired ministers and missionaries and provide all the comforts and conveniences possible for the residents at hardly any cost.

The Masonic Order, the Odd Fellows, the Elks, the Moose, and the Workmen's Circle, to mention only five of the fraternal orders, maintain homes for their aging members in all parts of the country. The homes are made available also to the wives or widows of former members. The entrance fees are adjusted to the financial means of the entrant and in many instances are completely waived.

The various unions and professional organizations also have homes for their aging members. There are set fees for applicants but for those who do not have the finances there are so-called "scholarships," where room, board and medical care are provided at a nominal fee or without any charge.

Among other types of homes notable in the services offered to residents are: Grey Gables, Ojai, Calif., catering to retired teachers; the Roosevelt Park Colony, Millville, N. J.; the Bleader Home for Colored in New York City; the Stovall Home, Los Angeles, Calif.; Senior Estates, Ryderwood, Wash.; and the Acacia Nursing Home, Ojai, Calif.

There are many more in cities and towns throughout the land that are operated on a commercial or an institutional basis, and new ones are being opened week after week. Some are independent, private or public housing, others offer a wide variety of out-of-home care. Among them are hotels catering to elderly guests with costs varying according to the location, the accommodations desired and the services rendered.

A list of such housing accommodations could be given in this book but it would be obsolete in a very short time because new places are being added too often to make the list workable. Whatever your needs you would do better to check with your local agencies, your Chamber of Commerce, social welfare office, Community House or Senior Citizens' Service Center, which will help you find the home you want, in keeping with your needs and ability to pay.

The smaller your income the more difficult it will be for you to find decent, adequate or desirable living quarters and the more careful you will have to be in your choice of a place in which to live.

Too many of the aged people are in the low income brackets and some means will have to be found through a Federal subsidy plan to support the building of low-cost, low-rent housing for the elderly. Such Federal subsidy, augmented by tax exemptions from each state and each county in the state, may encourage private capital and nonprofit corporations to build low-cost homes for the aged.

More and more attention is being given on a state and national level to those needs. You can help keep that interest alive by joining forces with other senior adults and stressing your needs over and over again to your selectmen, councilmen, assemblymen and members of your state senate as well as the congressmen and senators in Washington.

# CHAPTER THIRTEEN

# How to Instigate Proper Orientations

No one else can be concerned with, or show an interest in, your needs for mental care and in your problems of applicable psychological adjustments as much as you should be, even if you are in excellent physical and mental health now.

Make it a special project, if need be, to know what provisions there are in your city, county and state to give such psychological assistance, and what steps you or someone else of older age would have to take to get such help when needed. You may learn that yours is one of the many communities in the country which has few if any facilities to provide such assistance in times of need.

This may be due to a number of reasons. Among them are: (1) Insufficient public funds to maintain such help. (2) Few agencies set up to apply to and to secure from the services needed. (3) Lack of trained personnel and social workers interested in the problems of the aged to work in the field. (4) General public apathy toward the aged. (5) Lack of education and appreciation of the values and the potentialities of the senior adults in the community. (7) Opposition of certain groups to provide the necessary services to the aged.

As a matter of record, many states have no psychologists, psychiatrists, geriatricians and gerontologists connected in any way with the various social agencies so as to deal directly with the physical, mental and emotional problems of the aged, especially those who are not on relief rolls.

According to recent surveys, less than 60% of those past 65 years of age have health coverage. Even those who carry medical, surgical and hospitalization insurance on a group or individual basis do not have adequate coverage. It does not cover prolonged chronic degenerative ailments or mental illnesses that require psychological or psychiatric care.

The burden of such costs falls upon the individual who is often forced to use up whatever savings he has and mortgage everything he owns. And, when his own assets are depleted, he becomes the burden of his family or the responsibility of his community which is seldom equipped to meet his growing needs for medical care and attention.

The old, infirm person who is beset by physical disabilities and emotional problems, who is not completely destitute and is not as yet the ward of his community, is usually placed in a private or semi-private home, and there he finds himself in a pitiful plight. Only one fourth of all the registered and licensed rest homes, sanatoriums and so-called guest houses for the aged are considered adequate for the purposes intended. The rest are classified as "substandard" and range from the fair to the poor to the absolute slums.

Many of those places are terribly overcrowded. Six to eight beds are crammed into an average-size bedroom and the residents get little more than poorly planned and badly prepared food. This slipshod manner of caring for the residents often weakens and immobilizes many an older person who would otherwise be self-sufficient and able to care for himself.

The medical authorities, the health departments and the social welfare workers within those communities are fully aware of the existing deplorable conditions and would gladly do away with the substandard homes. But there are no other available accommodations and the homes are therefore licensed to operate.

Of course, many of those substandard homes could be improved. The owners would remodel the buildings, install safety features and extend their services if the income covered it. But, as surveys show, many of their residents subsisting on old-age assistance pay less than $100.00 a month for the services given and, on the basis of costs, little can be done at this time to better existing conditions.

Many communities close their eyes to these enervating conditions. The civic bodies and the public at large are content to let matters ride as is, but they forget to remember that the resultant physical and mental breakdown of the residents in the substandard homes becomes a staggering financial burden upon the community. It involves a fraction of the cost to care for someone who still has his health and his wits about him as compared to one who needs nursing, hospital or mental care.

Aside from the natural debilitating effects of older age and the demoralizing influence of substandard living which bring in their wake physical and mental ailments, many older people face other handicaps. Among them are enforced idleness, family neglect, lack of mental and occupational therapy, public indifference and the general assumption that the old are a useless and worthless lot.

The aftermath of these contributory factors has costly far-reaching effects. The senior adults have time to brood about the dreary drabness of their life, about the callous treatment in the rest homes, about the indifference of their respective families and the public at large. They feel forlorn, forsaken, and their resentments grow. These turn into rancor, bitterness, anger, animosity, and thus provide a fertile ground for breeding psychosomatic ailments and mental imbalances.

The ironic part of it is that many of such ailments could be prevented by simple inexpensive therapy methods. Some of them may call only for simplified programming, for the judicious use of modest recreational activities or rehabilitation procedures. At times it may call only for a sympathetic ear, for a simple change in daily routine, for a show of casual interest in the aged person.

This form of therapy for the residents of privately operated rest homes and nursing homes for the aged could be handled by volunteers recruited from schools, colleges and aids who usually work at clinics and hospitals at hardly any cost. Volunteers could also be solicited from senior adult groups to provide readers, companions, discussion leaders and visitors to such homes. A trained social worker, a gerontologist or a therapist could prepare a simple outline of things to do and follow.

This could well be something for you to take up in conjunction with several other men and women and become a most rewarding and satisfying objective to follow through. Keep in mind the fact that in many instances the aging person who feels he was abandoned needs only the reassurance that someone still wants him or cares for him. You can become the regenerating spirit to take him out of the doldrums and rekindle the fires of hope and faith and courage.

Among the men and women who need reassurance of their value to themselves and to others are those who because of economic dependence are forced to live with a married son or daughter. They are ever conscious of the tension in the air and bitterly resent the conditions that force them into sponging on a child and being in the way. They hate themselves for it and often wish themselves sickness or death. These engender inner conflicts, deep resentments, suppressed longings and find expression in these ways:

1—The aged parent, male or female, begins to brood more and more about the futility of living a useless life and of being a burden upon his children. He "lets go" of the will to resist the inroads of sickness or despondency and welcomes the opportunity of being removed from the home, of being placed in a hospital or a sanatorium. This, in turn, makes him a ripe subject for a mental casualty.

2—The aging parent assumes a defiant attitude toward the world at large and those around him. He strikes out at everything and everybody in sight. He becomes short-tempered, abusive, belligerent and demanding. He shows annoyance and displeasure at the slightest provocation. He becomes sensitized to normal noises and activities around him and is quick to voice his disapproval in loud terms to the discomfort of all concerned.

3—The aged parent develops a supersensitivity to pain and discomfort. A minor ache, ailment or disorder is magnified manifold and has to be given immediate care and professional attention. When the doctor summoned fails to agree with the gravity of the situation he is abused or vilified and hastily dismissed. The parent insists on seeing another doctor, starting a round of visitations. Pills and potions become a "must" in the life of the "old one" and soon afterwards the vicious circle is completed. A new hypochondriac has made his appearance to the despair of his family and all others around him.

4—The aging parent becomes autocratic and dictatorial. He begins to meddle in the ordinary affairs and routines of the home and insists that his wishes and ideas be followed or else he goes into anger tantrums or into sick-spells necessitating doctor visits and medical care. He deliberately "baits" or "needles" those around him and manages to involve the members of his family in his own inner conflicts and disillusionments. These build up needless tensions in the home and eventually lead to his own breakdown.

5—The aged person "kicks over the traces" and goes "all out" for fun, for pleasure, for "living it up." His new attitude is—no one cares for me, so the "heck" with my family and all the rest. If he has the cash he starts on one wild spree after another. He starts to throw his money away in a foolish, reckless fashion, daring anyone to interfere with his right to spend his money to suit himself. If he does not have the ready cash he forms strange friendships, enters into misalliances and eventually succeeds in making a mess of things for himself and the members of his family.

6—The aging person who has negotiable assets may turn to the other extreme, into a miser. He begins to suspect his family and friends of having designs on his money, of looking for ways to "fleece" him or defraud him or "do away" with him. He refuses to let go of a single dollar, even for his own needs. He sponges forever on friends and others and is quick to berate those who urge him to live and enjoy life. His suspicions and his sense of insecurity grow. The walls of distrust and estrangement which he erected between himself and those with whom he comes in contact day after day grow higher and higher. He withdraws into himself, begins to shun company and in his desire to escape reality becomes another mental casualty.

Do any of these conditions apply to you? If so and if the situation is too well entrenched, you may need outside help to correct matters. On the other hand, if you are aware of the irritating factors and feel you can help yourself, follow some or all of these suggestions:

1—Reappraise your position within the home of your child and learn to maintain a normal, natural outlook upon your relationship with every member of the family. You are there for one of these reasons. A. You have to live with them. If so, you must adapt yourself to their ways and do the best you can under the circumstances. B. You want to live with them. If so, you went into the arrangement with open eyes and should accept your son-in-law or daughter-in-law and the grandchildren at face value. C. They wanted you to live with them. If so, their intentions were good and if they happen to fall short of all your expectations be sure to make allowances for them.

2—Acknowledge the fact that you are no longer the head of the family. So, do not impose your will upon the rest. Do not try to dictate or to dominate and make yourself obnoxious in the process.

3—Accept your position in the home of your daughter or daughter-in-law in its true perspective and cultivate a "hands-off" attitude in matters which do not affect you personally.

4—Do not assume the role of a teacher or a censor, of a judge or a critic in the conduct of the home and in the ways which your grandchildren are taught to behave by their parents. They will like you for it and living together will be easier for all concerned.

5—Find things to do away from home where you can find enjoyment and relaxation, where you mingle with people of your age, where you can follow some of your interests and not be in the way of your daughter or your daughter-in-law.

6—Respect the rights of your daughter or son-in-law and their children. Do not inflict your friends upon them and do not invite people to meals or to other family functions without discussing matters beforehand. You would not tolerate it if someone were to do it to you. Why expect it from others?

7—Do not demand attention, consideration or obedience just because you ask for it. Do not expect to be catered to at all times because of your age or your money or whatever may be gained from you in material things. Respect and consideration are dependent upon reciprocity, upon a "give-and-take" action. And, in most instances, it is the older person, you for instance, who has to do most of the "giving." It is you who has to be pliable, agreeable and accommodating. It is you who has to "step back" and take second and even third place when it is expedient for the good of the family.

Follow some of these suggestions faithfully. They will engender better and happier feelings among you. They will also promote better relationships in your association with others and at the same time help you to retain your self-reliance and self-respect.

Your life expectancy today is greater than ever before in the history of man, and with every new day new ways are found to prolong your life. The number of men and women who will reach their seventies, eighties and even nineties is growing from year to year. Within this decade, the 1960s, we will have more than twenty million men and women past 65 years of age in the United States.

According to recent surveys based upon present conditions, approximately fifteen per cent of those senior adults will require continual medical or hospital care. Another twenty per cent will have one or more sense impairment or be partially disabled. They will need occasional medical care but the advances of their aging process, stemming from metabolic, arthritic, tumorous or from vascular system disorders will be arrested or controlled through palliative or constructive geriatrics.

This medical care for the 35% of the aged will involve expenditures which neither the individual, the members of his family nor the local community could possibly carry. The financing would have to come from the county and the state. Such funds could be raised only through new taxes and assessments that may place undue hardships upon businesses and home owners in such state, especially in the populous section of the country. The Federal government would have to step into the picture and render the help needed.

As for the 65% of the aged in fair physical and mental condition, they will remain self-sustaining and self-sufficient provided they are given the proper and adequate psychological help to maintain the right mental outlook toward themselves and the world around them. They will be free from psychosomatic ailments, able to carry on and be a credit to their respective communities if and when they are made to feel useful, accepted as total entities, allowed to participate in the life of their community, given the opportunity to meet people of their own age, and provided with the chance to find enjoyment and relaxation in various occupational and recreational activities.

These things cannot be left to the children of an aging parent or to the efforts of a local social welfare agency. It has to be handled on a state-wide and a national basis. Some states such as New York, Illinois, Michigan, Florida and

California, to mention only five, have county and state committees on aging to deal with the needs and the problems of the aged in their respective communities. Many cities throughout the country have well-established day centers where various activities are planned for every hour of the day.

For instance, the San Francisco Senior Center, which has over 700 members averaging 74 years of age, is supported by private and community funds. The fee for senior adults is only $1.00 a month. The center is open eight hours a day, six days a week. It is a beehive of activity from morning till night and is located next door to a public swimming beach. There are many classes in arts and crafts, languages, music appreciation and public speaking. There are bridge clubs, choral groups, social dancing, drama groups, holiday and birthday gatherings and various socializing events.

New York City, Chicago, Philadelphia, Cleveland, Newark, Pittsburgh, St. Petersburg, to mention only a few cities, have similar day centers. These have been instrumental in cutting down mental unrest and minor physical discomforts. They have also been helpful in reducing the call for medical care and nursing services by fostering the feeling of independence, by promoting the desire to keep going and engendering the sense of well-being even in the midst of pains and discomfort.

One of the notable day centers in the country is the Senior Adult Friendship Club at the Westside Jewish Community Center in Los Angeles. Among the six hundred and fifty members, in all walks of life, are some who came from mental institutions and many who were listless, despondent and seemingly helpless. Yet within months they regained their desire to live and are counted among the active ones. Others found miraculous cures for their mysterious ailments and gained a new lease on life. They made new friends, acquired new interests, developed hidden talents and blossomed out anew.

When asked for details, the director of the group, Sergei Nutkiewicz, said in part:

"Our basic aim is to help older people find common interests and activities within the limitations of their age. We encourage active participation in various cultural, educational, artistic and recreational endeavors.

"We have classes in swimming, in creative dancing, in arts and crafts, in languages and in music appreciation. We foster dramatic groups, chorales, musicals, book reviews and current affairs discussions. We have nature study groups, classes in gerontology, folk and square dancing and a literary circle. There are also frequent social gatherings, birthday celebrations, community singing and general socializing and get-acquainted meetings.

"Our activities begin on Monday morning with a meeting of the executive board, chosen by the membership at large, and continue for the rest of the day and for the balance of the week, with special events scheduled for one or more evenings a week.

"In addition to the manifold doings at the center, there are picnics, excursions, theatre parties, overnight trips, week-end vacations and other outdoor activities geared to certain times of the year. In each case we try to involve as many people as possible by having them serve on various committees or assume responsibilities. We strive to make every member feel that he is useful, that he belongs and is important to himself and to others. This promotes self-assurance and self-confidence.

"All of these activities are supported by private and communal funds. Hence, the cost to senior adults is less than thirty-five cents a week."

If such facilities are available in your town be sure to take advantage of them. If not, join forces with other people of your age and try to promote the establishment of a similar center. This could conceivably become your major project and what satisfaction it would bring to see something like this become a reality in your home town!

What are some of the steps you can take in the meantime to foster the proper psychological balance and to adjust yourself emotionally to things and conditions around you? The following suggestions may seem general in scope but they are basically sound and you would do well to adapt some or all of them to your needs:

1—Be ever on guard to keep well. You are old enough to know, without caution from your doctor or from others, that you have to be more careful nowadays in all of your daily habits and activities. The old adage, "The old gray mare ain't what she used to be" applies to all older people and you are no exception.

2—Be ever on guard against needless emotional upsets, against outbursts of temper and against building up foolish resentments. Those things work havoc with normal bodily functions and can do you great harm emotionally. Be wise enough to let little annoyances and petty grievances pass you by. Be old enough to overlook small failings and shortcomings and refuse to take a stand on trivial issues.

3—Be ever on guard against nurturing needless fears, worries or anxieties. As time goes by, and you have it to spare, there may be a tendency on your part to become too apprehensive about your health or your looks, about your family or your friends, about life or conditions around you. If you can change some of those things, well and good. If you cannot, accept them as they are and make the most of what you CAN do.

4—Be sure to take the middle of the road in whatever you do or contemplate doing. Do not become a zealot or a fanatic and let anything become a matter of life and death to you. Your battles are already won and this is the time for you not to fight life but to enjoy it.

5—Be ready to accept your status as a senior adult. Stop fighting the visible manifestations of your age and do not ignore the sensible precautions to be taken because of your advancing years. There is charm, beauty, dignity and meaning in age. Look for them, capitalize upon them and benefit by them.

6—Be sure to take up appropriate hobbies and activities. Give your hands and mind things to do. Keep them both active and you will surely maintain a desirable mental and emotional balance. There are numerous ways for you to broaden your aspects, to widen your visions, to enlarge your circle of friends. Time and opportunity are in your favor. Use them and let them add to your enjoyment of living.

7—Map the course of your activities for several months in advance and set certain schedules for yourself to follow. For instance, plan to spend one or two evenings a week studying or learning something in company with others. It could be a class in languages, in the liberal arts, in public speaking or in human relations. Set aside another evening each week to attend fraternal or other social meetings. Then have one or more evenings a week to be with friends and further your social contacts.

Set aside two or three mornings or afternoons each week to do desirable things at home, to follow a given hobby, to visit with neighbors or be helpful to someone else. Spend at least one day a week away from your usual surroundings by taking trips in your local buses and streetcars to outlying sections and walk part of the way back home. Assume that you are a stranger in your town and join "sight-seeing" trips to points of interest in and around your home town. Or take leisurely trips to the country, to the seashore or to the mountains in your own car and arrange to spend at least one night a month overnight somewhere away from home.

8—Take advantage of seasonal doings in your city and in nearby places. Go to sport events, races, outlying movie houses and drive-in theatres, little theatres, fiestas, county fairs, concerts and various exhibitions, even when the doings in themselves are of little interest to you. Offer your services to your community as a juror, precinct worker during election time or as a volunteer aide to some civic or charitable group.

9—If you are married, be sure to include your spouse as your escort or companion, and wherever possible make it a twosome, unless the event is strictly for males or females. At the same time, leave room for yourself to be with others of your own sex from time to time. As a man, arrange to go fishing, hiking, camping, or playing a friendly game of cards with other men. As a woman, plan to join other women at special meetings, fashion shows, sewing bees, mah jong games and other activities of special interest to women.

10—Learn to see your age in its four-dimensional aspects. A. *As the chronological age.* The calendar years of your life are the accepted measure of age but they in themselves have little significance. It is how you take your years that counts. Some people are old at forty, others are young at seventy. B. *As the biological age.* The condition of your heart, your organs and your various bodily functions may stamp you as an older or a younger person. This is where you and your doctor can work together to keep you much younger than you are.

C. *As your social age.* The interests you have, the activities you follow, the contacts you have, and the people with whom you associate establish the measure of your age. D. *As your mental age.* Your attitude towards life and people in general, your ways of thinking and behaving have a great deal to do with the way your age affects you. As a matter of fact, it is in these two aspects, the social and the mental age, that you set the pace for yourself and make your choice, because it is not how OLD you are but HOW you are old.

These are some of the ways in which you can instigate the proper psychological adjustment in your life and thereby learn how to find the gold in your golden age.

CHAPTER FOURTEEN

# How to Cope with Minor
# Mental Problems

A mental disorder is a sickness of the mind. It has the same relation to the health and welfare of the human organism as any physical sickness. It may come with birth, such as mongolism or microcephalia, in the same way that a prenatal physical deformity occurs, or it may be contracted later in life.

In other words, a mental illness may be due to physiological reasons, to disease, to a tumor on the brain, to organic impairments or to an arrested mental development. It may be due to glandular disturbances. Biochemists and neurologists contend that mental illness can be caused by "adrenoxine," an adrenalin decomposant which for still unknown reasons is not properly metabolized in normal bodily functions. Or, it may be due to an induced fixed attitude, to an acquired frame of mind, to overwork or overanxiety, to mounting difficulties at work or at home, or to a growing involutional reaction toward people and the world around you.

Mental illness in any and all of its categories may range from the mild to the severe, from the passive to the violent form. For instance, among the mentally deficient there are four gradations. The weak-minded simpleton, the innocuous moron, the usually harmless imbecile and the unpredictable idiot, who may remain passive and harmless for a long time and then suddenly, for no apparent reason, become violent, belligerent, abusive and even homicidal.

Even the seemingly sane and normal individual who never had any mental disturbance can often lose himself in a fit of temper and in the grip of his uncontrollable fury do something horrible, despicable, and at times commit a brutal murder. Yet, when he is brought to trial he could conceivably be exonerated for his acts if his defense can substantiate claims of a momentary mental blackout, of what is usually called "temporary insanity."

A mental disturbance, even in its mildest form, usually leads to emotional instability. The actions and reactions of such a person become unpredictable and if the contributing factors continue to aggravate the growing imbalance it may lead to a compulsion or a complex, to a phobia or a delusion, to a mania or to a psychosis.

A psychosis is a severe form of a mental illness which cannot come upon you unexpectedly. Unlike a physical sickness caused by an infection, by poison or by an accident, which may incapacitate you almost instantly, a mental ailment, unless it is due to a head injury or an undetected brain tumor, takes time to develop. It is usually preceded by recognized symptoms and among them are:

1—The growing reluctance to face daily tasks and problems and the evident attempts to run away from reality and responsibility.

2—The delusion that the world is against you, that everybody is deliberately "picking" on you, and therefore you must be ready to fight anyone and everyone.

3—The inability to reach a decision, even on some trifling everyday matter, especially if there is more than one way to handle it.

4—The tendency to see only the black, bleak side of life and nurture moods of depression and despondency.

5—The acquired habit of alternating between depression and exultation, between immobility and restless, feverish activity, with hardly a break between them.

6—The inability to sleep, rest, relax or overlook the minor, petty annoyances of everyday living.

7—The loss of interest in your job, friends, family, surroundings and personal appearance.

8—The tendency to be touchy, irritable, overemphatic and to lose your temper at the slightest provocation.

9—The urge to keep on talking and jump from one subject to another in a bewildering fashion, without regard to the time, place, listeners and justifiable interruptions.

10—The readiness to suspect or to accuse, condemn or berate those who do not fully and quickly agree with what you are saying or implying.

11—The promptness to spend money far above your means or to give it away recklessly, contrary to common sense and the sound advice of your friends and family.

12—The inability to "stay put" for any length of time and the compulsion to be "on the go" or do something.

13—The readiness to take up strange cults, support weird groups, finance crazy fads, develop strange interests or indulge in questionable activities.

14—The acquisition of childish fears or the development

of a hypersensitivity to common noises, certain foods, children, given groups, to ideas or customary routines.

15—The growing delusion that you hear, see, feel or reach for things which no one else but you can do.

Any one or more of these symptoms when allowed to dominate your thoughts and affect your actions can become entrenched as a psychosis which may require lengthy, costly psychotherapy to be cured.

Psychiatrists place psychosis in four general cateogries, each having its fluctuating degrees of severity which may or may not respond to a given method of treatment. These are: (1) Schizophrenia. (2) Involutional Psychosis. (3) Manic Depressive Psychosis. (4) Old-age Psychosis.

## Schizophrenia

This is a breakdown in personality and a gradual loss of customary thinking and normal realistic behavior. It involves delusions or hallucinations, regressions or various unpredictable actions and reactions. It often leads to a split, to the formation of a double or triple personality, each with its own traits, personality, characteristics and complemental behavior. Robert Louis Stevenson dramatized one of those dual personality situations in his memorable story, *Dr. Jekyll and Mr. Hyde*.

There are four types of schizophrenia:

A. Simple Schizophrenia. The patient loses cognizance of his usual life, routines and surroundings and distorts all reality. He may become as helpless as a baby and absolutely dependent upon others. And, as the sickness progresses, gradually turns into a human "vegetable."

B. Hebephremic Schizophrenia. The patient assumes the

actions and mentality of a child. He prattles happily or is interested only in children's games and toys and often has fits of nonsensical giggles. He loses all contact with his own adulthood and the real world around him.

C. Catatonic Schizophrenia. The patient may remain rigid or motionless for hours at a time. He may stare vacantly in space before him and be totally oblivious of life and movement all around him. Or, he may develop strange tics and twitches, pace back and forth like a caged animal or thrash about aimlessly in his bed.

D. Paranoid Schizophrenia. The patient suffers from strange delusions or hallucinations. He hears voices, sees visions, has disturbing sensations or follows voiceless orders to do weird, inexplicable things. He may assume the character of a fictional or an historical figure, look upon himself as a creature from some other age or world, believe that all those around him want to hurt him or "do away" with him and may develop uncontrollable homicidal tendencies. Strangely enough, his delusions of grandeur or his fears of persecution may be persistently logical and therefore may be difficult to cure.

### Involutional Psychosis

In this type of mental illness the patient is subject to deep depressions. He may have fits of weeping and lamentations, be beset with overpowering anxieties and feel that life is not worth living. He may complain of painful sensations or develop serious psychosomatic ailments difficult to diagnose and just as difficult to treat.

### Manic-Depressive Psychosis

In this form of mental illness the patient swings from a deep depression to ebullient elation and may alternate between the two extremes within minutes of each other. He may chatter away for hours and elaborate upon various grandiose ideas or he may wallow in a mood of despondency and hardly open his mouth. These unpredictable abrupt changes in mood may last for days at a time or change from hour to hour.

## Old-age Psychosis

This form of psychosis may be due to senility or to cerebral arteriosclerosis. Both have the same symptoms and are difficult to tell apart. The patient acts like a child, loses control over normal body functions, foregoes all personal modesty and adult behavior. He may "act out" his childish delusions or he may assume a lascivious pose, make improper advances to those around him or expose himself indecently time after time. He may develop childish tantrums and sulk for hours or loudly demand constant services and attention. He may lose all sense of lucidity, keep asking the same silly questions over and over again or just fall apart and become a raving lunatic. His actions may become more and more violent and he may require enforced restrictions.

Various physical sicknesses such as rabies, smallpox, diphtheria, typhus, dysentery, yellow fever and similar infectious diseases respond to serum treatments. Others call for antibiotics, for a change in diet or climate, while still others require surgery and long periods of convalescence.

Mental illness follows the same general pattern. It can be mild or severe, easy to treat or difficult to deal with and at times incurable. A given mental illness can be cured successfully and later reappear in a similar or more severe form. But this should not be considered more alarming than a recurrence of any physical sickness or organic disorder.

Medical science has advanced enormously within the last fifty years. Many dreaded plagues of the past have been stopped or completely eliminated through preventive injections, through inoculations and modern sanitation practices. Unfortunately, no way has as yet been found to inoculate anyone against a nervous breakdown or a mental disorder. The more complex our social order grows, the more wants are aroused, the more we seek to improve our living conditions and get more material comforts, the greater the tensions and the greater the tendency to mental strain and disturbances.

Mental illness often begins with the nurture of a resentment or with the overindulgence of an emotion. Let any feeling or desire, any grievance or annoyance linger long enough with you. Give it time and attention. Exaggerate its effects or significance. Endow it with special values or meaning and you will have the "makings" of a complex. Let that complex gain prominence and it will lead to a mental disturbance.

At times a given mental illness is a cover-up for something which was repressed a long time back and perhaps completely forgotten. It retreated into the subconscious to build up strength and eventually erupts as a sickness with all the symptoms of a mental derangement, difficult to retrace and necessitating lengthy psychiatric analysis and treatment.

The mentally ill person is edged in by inflated egotism, by strange delusions, by constant irritations or by induced abnormal behavior. He is unpredictable in his actions and various responses and is a total stranger even to himself.

The first symptoms of a mental illness may be in a sudden oversensitivity, in becoming quickly upset by little things, in an emotional let-down, in fits of despondency, in a tendency to flare up at the slightest provocation, in growing apprehensions or in the inexplicable desire to stay away from contacts with others.

As these symptoms manifest themselves and the strange reactions grow, the mentally disturbed person either runs away from people or is forever seeking the company of others. He may maintain a stony silence most of the time or stare vacantly into space or he may seek others to chatter to incessantly, to their annoyance. He may try to do bodily harm to others or do away with himself.

He may develop a sudden dislike for working at a given job, for being with certain people or for doing anything. He may assume that the whole world is against him and lash out at everything in sight. In time he may refuse to face reality and in his desire to run away from life and its responsibilities retreat into a private world of his own where reality is replaced by dreams and fantasy.

The underlying reasons for his mental breakdown may be near at hand or totally obscure. The illness may be a neurosis fairly simple to deal with or it may grow into a psychosis calling for hospitalization, for lengthy psychiatric treatments or for enforced segregation from others.

To paraphrase the famous psychiatrist Dr. Karl Meninger: ". . . Mental illness is a sickness which can strike anyone at any time. We used to think of the mentally sick as being insane and completely irresponsible for their acts or behaviors. We usually associated them with the violent forms of dementia praecox, with overwhelming passions, with deep depressions, with overpowering delusions, with paralyzing fears, with homicidal tendencies or with uncontrollable atavistic impulses.

"But such is not the case at all times. Many of us who are considered sane, normal and sensible have symptoms of mental illness in one form or another. It is to be found in our inhibitions, in sudden bursts of temper, in irrational fears, in fits of dejection, in self-appointed moralisms, in preconceived notions guarded with zeal, and in various other social misbehaviors. These symptoms may be mild, severe or in-between and the degree of such mental disturbance will fluctuate from time to time.

"The old belief that mental illness is incurable has been dispelled years ago. Nowadays, even in entrenched cases of psychosis, whether it be simple, hebephrenic, catatonic or paranoic schizophrenia, many cures are effected. In some cases the patient needs psychosurgery or shock therapy or psychotherapy. In other cases only psychoanalysis augmented by sympathy and understanding is sufficient for the purpose . . ."

Mental illness is on the increase. It is estimated that one out of every ten persons in the United States suffers from some form of mental sickness requiring competent treatment. Unfortunately there are not enough professional men and sufficient facilities to meet those growing needs.

There have been many schools of psychiatry since Dr. Sigmund Freud first formulated his theories of the unconscious. They began with his former pupils, Alfred Adler and Carl Jung, and were followed by such outstanding psychologists and psychiatrists at Otto Rank, Sandor Ferenczi, Frieda Fromm-Reichmann, Karen Horney, Eric Fromm, Wilhelm Reich, J. B. Watson, Harry Stack Sullivan and others. They differed widely in their views and interpretations. Furthermore, there is dissension in the ranks and considerable disagreement between professionals and between laymen as to the values of psychoanalysis in treating mental illness. Some look upon such treatments as a form of brainwashing while others see it as a glorified mental healing process and ask provocative questions.

Among the questions are: (1) Is it not possible that mental illness is due mainly to chemical changes in the body? (2) Should treatments combine the physiological as well as the psychological approach? (3) Is illness of the mind due only to distorted memories of the past, to general emotional upsets or to other causes? (4) Can childhood repressions continue to affect the adult? (5) Is introversion due only to environment or also to induced mental attitudes? (6) What part does habit acquired by design or by accident play in the formation of a complex or fixation? (7) How much of today's mental illnesses are due to the complexity of life? (8) Should the analyst look for current underlying causes or grope only for the forgotten grudges and grievances?

These challenging questions cannot be set aside. They arouse considerable arguments among laymen and among professionals. There is no doubt that modern psychiatry has cured thousands of mentally sick people. Yet there are numerous cases on record where a mentally disturbed person unable to get the necessary psychiatric help let Mother Nature take her natural course in using her own corrective measures and eventually enabled him to regain his mental balance.

One of the problems facing us today is the steadily growing number of the mentally ill among senior adults. Few provisions have been made to meet their needs on an adequate basis and whatever help they get on a local level is pitifully small and insufficient.

Among the factors which contribute to the senior adult's mental imbalance are: (1) His growing physical impairments which are the natural consequence of older age but which he has not as yet learned to accept as normal and inevitable. (2) His reduced income which prevents him from seeking and getting needed medical care, good food and decent living accommodations. (3) His resentments of the general attitude toward him as a "has been," as an oldster who is no longer needed or wanted. (4) His growing dependence upon others as his physical abilities decline. (5) His growing awareness of the widespread indifference by civic bodies, public officials and the general public toward his needs and his problems.

The saddest part of this general indifference toward the older adult lies in the fact that we place youth on a pedestal and completely ignore the inexorable march of time. We refuse to admit that the young, too, shall be old some day and shall also need help, sympathy, consideration and understanding.

The general belief of the public at large is that as soon as anyone passes his 65th birthday he turns into a liability to himself and to others around him. He is immediately classified as being "expendable" and is looked upon as a creature apart from and different from all those who are under 65 years of age.

For instance, it is assumed that anyone past 65 no longer needs the proper food, the right clothing, adequate medical care, decent housing or any of the usual comforts of living. His ability to see, think, feel, work, judge, understand and appreciate is supposed to be gone, and therefore he is no longer entitled to consideration as an individual, as a living, pulsating human being. He is presumed to be a "dead weight" and is allowed to live on only because he can no longer be driven off into the forests, thrown from cliffs into raging seas or sealed in airless caves, as was the custom not so many years ago.

Does that sound impossible to believe? Is it too fantastic? Not so, when you talk to members of the younger generation and to some public officials who look down with disdain upon the old and have little use for the aging members of their communities.

To counteract the existing attitudes and to retain a semblance of dignity and self-respect, many an older person, especially one forced to live with children, often becomes overly aggressive. He demands extra care, attention and solicitude from those around him and when such fail to materialize, grows despondent, starts to nurture deep resentments, and consciously or unconsciously begins to look for ways to enforce extra care and attention. His frame of mind becomes a fertile soil for mental illness and soon afterwards he turns into a psychosomatic casualty.

If you are mentally disturbed and need psychiatric care, you may find the cost prohibitive for you. Visits with psychiatrists, whether on an hourly or semi-hourly basis, aside from the cost of prescribed medications or required surgical and hospital care, range from $20.00 to $50.00 a visit. A given mental case may call for two or more visits a week and extend for a period of months or years. This places such psychiatric treatments out of reach for many people and more so for senior adults who have a reduced fixed income.

Among the therapies favored by analysts and psychiatrists are psychobiological, gestalt, directive, nondirective, conditional, reflex, rational, reciprocal, inhibitive and family therapy. Some of them are called the "red light district" of psychoanalysis. This book does not undertake to evaluate any one of these or other psychoanalytical practices. It will deal briefly with six of the current techniques, to serve only as information for the reader. These are: (1) The Free Association Technique. (2) Psychosurgery. (3) Electric Shock Treatments. (4) The Uses of Modern Drugs. (5) Hypnotherapy. (6) Group Psychotherapy.

## Free Association

In the "free association" technique, the patient is encouraged to think aloud and to talk about anything he wishes. He is urged to speak about his work or his family, his dreams and aspirations, his hobbies and diversions, his peeves and his resentments, his likes and dislikes, his hopes and disappointments, his amoral urges and conscious repressions.

As he continues to put his ordinary thoughts into words he loosens up. He finds himself talking freely and gradually exposes his hidden emotional disturbances. Before long he develops a so-called dependency known as a "regression," and reverts emotionally to his childhood days.

This leads him to the "projection" stage. He begins to attribute special curative powers to his analyst with the expectation to be relieved almost immediately of all his tensions and mental imbalance. When the analyst cannot accomplish the feat the patient often grows more despondent and discouraged.

The "projection" stage often leads the patient to form a mistaken identity, to the unconscious distortion known as the "transference." This is where, in the patient's eye, the analyst assumes the physical aspects of the stern father, the kind mother, the protective older brother or sister, the exacting teacher, the mean boss, the accusing judge, the nagging spouse, the lost friend, the missing sweetheart or the longed-for love. As such, the analyst becomes the embodiment of the mental image with all of its attendant hatreds, fears, resentments, loves and desires.

The love angle where the patient seeks physical and emotional gratification in the person of the analyst often presents a delicate problem. He has to divert the love role thrust upon him in a way that will not instigate a new emotional upset and disturb the neutral patient-analyst relationship.

The troublesome "transference" stage is passed when under the guidance of the analyst the patient goes through one or more "abreactions." These refer to the recall of painful emotional experiences that are finally exposed to the light of day. This enables the patient to reach a "catharsis," meaning a relief or the removal of his disturbing mental imbalance and a gradual release from its damaging influence.

With such exposure effected, the analyst can point out to the patient how and why his neurosis came about. He can also recommend specific steps to minimize or to remove the underlying causes and thereby eliminate the mental disturbance.

This process of inducing free, uninhibited talk and frank exposure of repressed feelings and emotions, known as psychoanalysis, is effective in many cases. They are helpful to the neurotic but in most instances much less to the psychotic. He often needs other forms of psychotherapy, such as psychosurgery or electric shock treatments, energizing pills or injections, to be supplemented by educational and occupational therapy.

### Psychosurgery

In cases of severe mental disturbance and in certain forms of psychosis, psychosurgery is advisable. In the past, the surgeon performed a prefrontal lobotomy by cutting the white nerve fibers which connect the frontal lobe of the brain with the thalamus, through the back of the head. Nowadays, however, surgeons use an easier and surer method. They perform a topectomy. The brain surface is exposed from above the cortex and the specified prefrontal areas are removed, in the predetermined manner. The purpose of such surgery is to sever the connections between the respondent nerve fibers and the "emotional control center," the thalamus.

Since this was written, a new technique in performing prefrontal lobotomies was developed by Dr. Peter Lindstrom, a neurosurgeon at the University of Utah. He calls it PST (Prefrontal Sonic Treatment). Three holes are drilled in the patient's skull and through them beams of silent ultra-sonic waves of high range are directed into the nerve fibers to invalidate them. The tiny bone buttons are then put back and they gradually grow back into place.

These operations slow down reflex action, quiet the difficult-to-manage psychotic and make him more amenable to various psychiatric treatments. However, there are cases on record where a lobotomy did not produce the desired results. In some instances there were new emotional complications and aberrations. The surgery loosened repressed feelings, released disquieting inhibitions, increased the violence of old tantrums and resulted in new mental disorders. Fortunately, these cases are the exception and many a topectomy becomes the only way to help a psychotic and restore him to normalcy.

### Electric Shock Treatment

The deliberate induction of convulsion, of temporary violent muscular spasms, through the use of drug injections and electric plate conductors, usually designated as EST treatments, is in wide use nowadays. Although electric shock treatments are associated with mental institutions they are often given to outpatients in a clinic or in a doctor's office. The patient comes in the morning and leaves for home later in the day.

Some people have a mistaken notion about EST. They believe that electro-shock treatments harm the nervous system. But such is not the case. Records and tests conducted over many years disclose no complications, show no changes in one's personality and no damage to normal emotional and psychological reactions. On the contrary, many recorded instances indicate a noticeable improvement in judgment and in emotional stability.

Several forms of EST are used nowadays. There is the convulsive and the semi-convulsive type. Injections of insulin or metrazol are used in connection with electro-conductive plates to send currents of electricity through the patient's brain. There is also the photo-shock treatment. The patient is given a small dose of Azozol. An intermittently flickering light is then placed in front of his eyes to induce cerebral stimulation. The patient soon goes into a seizure but it is not so convulsive as the others. Furthermore, it lends itself to a better study of the shock effects upon his brain waves.

EST has been very helpful in "involutional melancholy," in depressions brought about by deep anxieties or by imbedded resentments, by entrenched fears or by emotional disturbances, which may be tied in with the climacteric period in men or the menopause in women. As a rule, several electro-shock treatments are given close together and they often effect the desired results.

However, in manic-depressive cases where suicidal tendencies are present or where there are complications of an organic or emotional nature such as delusions, hallucinations, hypochondria, to mention only three of them, there may be a need for quite a few EST treatments, and they in turn may have to be supplemented by other psychotherapies.

In most cases, before EST treatments are undertaken, the patient must undergo a thorough physical and mental examination, and the examining physican or psychiatrist may recommend the use of anti-depressants in lieu of EST.

## Drugs

In evaluating the uses of drugs to combat mental illness, Dr. Robert A. Moore, psychiatrist with the University of Michigan, said in part: "Psychoactive drugs such as tranquilizers, stimulants, suppressants and anti-depressants, have made mental hospitals more quiet and patients more accessible to other forms of treatment. The drugs cut down electroshock therapy and psychosurgery. But they do *not* offer definitive treatment, since mental illness is a form of maladaptive reaction within the framework of lifelong patterns of behavior. Those patterns must be modified before cures can be effected . . ."

A tremendous number of such drugs is in use today. Among the first phenothiazines in the rauwolfia field was "Chlorpromazine." A competitive product was "Reserpine" but it produced such side effects as fainting, sinus disorders and depressive moods.

The meprobamate tranquilizers were then introduced. Those best known are "Miltown" and "Equanil." Others in wide use are "Meratran," "Milpath," "Meprosan 400," "Deprol," the emylcome "Straitan," the thioridazine "Mellaril" and the chlordiazepoxide "Librium."

These pills can be bought only with a bona fide prescription but because of their wide appeal and seeming effectiveness enjoy a tremendous black market sale and literally millions of them are taken daily to offset the "blues," combat fatigue or sleeplessness, lessen "hangovers" and counteract so-called "let-downs."

Used under strict supervision and supplemented by psychotherapy these drugs will relieve nervous spasms and hypersecretions and allay tensions or mental anxieties. Through them, the psychotic is easier to manage and becomes more conducive to various treatments and psychotherapy. Through them, the neurotic is led to find surcease from tensions as the pills tend to calm and soothe his troubled mind. But the beneficial values of such pills are transitory and in some instances have unexpected side effects. Among them are prolonged drowsiness, a dullness of sensory perception, a slow-down of natural reflexes, a growing disregard or indifference for normal safety precautions, a loss in sensitivity to pain and a tendency to become quickly and easily depressed.

Aside from such possible side effects, the greater danger in the continual use of these drugs, without control and supervision, lies in the fact that they are not curative agents but palliatives. They can easily become a "crutch" to lean upon, the mask to hide the true nature of the ailment and its contributing factors. The deadening effect of the pills may aggravate the existing condition, deepen its hold upon the person involved and lead to a greater and more serious mental aberration.

One of the newest drugs in the same field is LSD (lysergic acid). It is used as a substitute for psychoanalysis and many spectacular cures are attributed to it. However, little is known about all of its side effects and until such are fully recorded and evaluated, many doctors are hesitant in prescribing LSD for wider use.

A number of other bio-chemical wonder drugs, with the generic name of "psychic energizers" are used nowadays. One of those energizers is "Marsalid." It is used in lieu of electro-shock treatments to deal with a depressive mania. However, one of its side effects is possible disruption of normal liver functions and doctors are careful in its use. There is also a number of other anti-depressants, such as "Nardil," "Tofra-nil," and "Parnate," to mention only three of them.

If you need tranquilizing or energizing pills, do not, under any circumstance, start taking them on your own cog-nizance. Be sure to consult your doctor and let him do the prescribing. He will check into your personal allergies, your metabolistic or hypersensitive reactions before giving you a prescription. This will forestall unfavorable side effects and possible damage to your physical and nervous systems.

### Hypnotherapy

One of the techniques popular at this time is hypno-therapy. It is the applied power of directive suggestion to place the patient in a receptive state of mind and put him in a "trance." Hypnotherapy has these basic benefits: (1) It promotes ease of tension and relaxation. (2) It induces sus-ceptibility to follow suggestions made. (3) It encourages the insight into personal problems and the urge to expose repudi-ated feelings and emotions. (4) It fosters temporary depend-ence upon the hypnotist, dissipates one's sense of helplessness and tends to satisfy repressed wishes.

To be effective in its application the subject must be willing to follow suggestions, within certain limitations, and be ready to subordinate his will to the suggestions given to him by the hypnotist. And, his susceptibility is increased with the extent of the hypnotic trance.

The first stage begins when the subject is asked to stare at something or to fix his gaze at a moving or stationary shiny object. And while concentrating on it, the hypnotist keeps suggesting that the subject relax, that his eyes are growing heavier and that he is feeling sleepy. The shiny object and the droning voice build up a growing receptivity. Before long the subject closes his eyes, drops off to sleep and enters the initial trance of hypnosis.

The second stage, the medium trance, is where the subject, apparently asleep, responds readily to given suggestions. For instance, if told that it is too cold or too warm in the room, or that he is hungry, thirsty, sad, happy, angry or elated, he reacts accordingly. He readily accepts the suggestions that he is tasting, drinking, eating, touching, feeling or holding something and is quick to respond to it in the normal and natural manner, as if the suggestion was a fact.

In the third step, the deep trance, the subject may be told to go back into his past. He may be asked to describe a childhood incident, to relive a traumatic experience, to recall an embarrassing moment or to talk about things which troubled him in the past. His response may be just what is desired as he gives a quick, true description of something which he formerly repressed.

In the final stage, the somnabulistic trance, the subject readily accepts all situations and sensations suggested. Thus, at the order of the hypnotist, he will see and hear only what he is told to see and hear, regardless of what else may transpire in his presence. He will sense and experience the feelings and emotions suggested, even when such are the exact opposite of his usual actions and behavior. He may also be led to

"act out" his hidden fears, sorrows, guilt, delusions or com-
pulsions or other mental disturbances and through such uninhibited exposure enable himself and the attending hypnotist
to see his troubles in their proper light. This may lead him
to recognize them as foolish falacies and gradually eliminate them.

Hypnotherapy has another important benefit. Aside from
the immediate response to suggestions given, the hypnotist
can implant ideas and modes of behavior to be acted upon
at a later date. These posthypnotic suggestions retain their
effectiveness for some time and in this manner can influence
the actions and reactions of the subject along desired, specified lines.

Hypnosis, however, cannot be used on all persons. Some,
because of their sceptical or analytical nature, because of
their incapacity to focus attention or the unconscious opposition to hypnosis, will not respond.

A hypnotic trance can be used to remove an emotional
block or to "act out" without restraint some bothersome situation. It can ease strain and anxiety. It can minimize the
effects of, and often eliminate, psychosomatic ailments. It can
displace nondesirable habits, debilitate conditioned reflexes
and wholly rebuild a person's personality. It can utilize age
regression or age progression by moving the person under
hypnosis backward or forward in time, and thereby observe
and evaluate how he would behave under given circumstances.

But hypnosis in itself is not a cure for mental illness. It
can mitigate the outward symptoms of a given neurosis or of
a psychosomatic ailment, but unless it also reaches the underlying causes and removes them there can be no cure. A symptom is only the noticeable manifestation of an inner conflict.

The removal of such symptom may only force the conflict to mask itself and induce the development of other symptoms more difficult to treat or to control.

## Group Psychotherapy

Generally speaking, there are six main categories of group therapy where participants are brought together to "work out" mutual problems. The basic purposes of such meetings is to combine efforts in a one-for-all and all-for-one method, to encourage informal free group discussion, to uncover the basic reasons for mental imbalance and to help participants to function more effectively within the framework of their respective mental limitations. These categories are:

### A. The Didactic Group

The group sessions are handled in a systematized pre-determined educational manner. The therapist chooses the topic related in some way to the basic underlying reasons or problems of the participants and limits group expression to the subject matter he selected for that particular meeting.

### B. The Socio-therapeutic Group

The members of the group plan and "carry out" organized activities of an educational or recreational character to meet their own preferences. The therapist remains in the background as an observer or, if called upon to do so, as an occasional advisor.

### C. The Repressive-Inspirational Group

The members arrange matters to suit the expressed wishes of the majority. The sessions consist mainly of accounts of personal experiences, how certain problems were encountered and how such were met and nullified. It is a form of testimonial, a public confession. The basic purpose is to encour-

age other members of the group to "open up," to face themselves, as it were. This method of group therapy has been
used successfully by such groups as the Alcoholics Anony-
mous.

### D. The Psycho-Dramatic Group

Under the guidance of the therapist, the members present
dramatized versions of typical problems and situations which
one or more of those present is facing at the moment. Everyone at the meeting is encouraged to take an active part in the
presentations and "act out" their respective roles and possible solutions.

### E. Occupational Therapy

The therapist involves each person present on an individualized or on a collective basis in one or more occupational activity adapted to the needs or the desires, to the interests or the inclinations of the participant. If it is a creative
effort the members of the group are encouraged to express
themselves freely and vent their displeasures or resentments
in the work undertaken.

### F. The Free Interaction Group

These are specially oriented free discussion sessions
where all members are encouraged to the open interchange
of ideas and the discussion of existing feelings and emotions.
The therapist may comment from time to time or pose an
occasional question but otherwise exercises no control over
the proceedings.

The six categories of psychotherapeutic group methods
are often interwoven. The mentally disturbed person is urged
to follow his particular interest and is also encouraged to venture into other fields so as to derive the greatest possible value
from each meeting. He may be shown how to "work off"

anger and hostility through physical effort and how to vent his spite and his animosities upon inanimate objects, without harm to himself or to other people around him.

In the "talk sessions" the therapist often acts as moderator. He urges every person in the small group to "talk out" his hidden feelings, his repressed emotions, with the assurance that there shall be no censure or condemnation. During such sessions, held for an hour or more, once or several times a week at the discretion of the therapist, each person can unburden his troubles, as it were, upon the rest. Then the listeners, under the guidance of the therapist-moderator, are free to make comments, to express their sympathy or understanding, or to suggest ways how to cope with the existing burden.

The "talk sessions" in themselves cannot solve a given problem or eliminate the contributing factors. They can only uncover an existing disturbing situation. But the exposure and the free exchange of ideas, of comments and suggestions, may reveal the underlying reasons. That, in turn, may help the particular individual. It may show him the way to live with conditions he cannot change and how to correct matters where changes can be made.

How can you tell when someone is on the verge of a mental breakdown? How can you tell when you are reaching a mental impasse? There are many indications. Among them are: (1) You find it more and more difficult to get along with others. (2) You lose your composure too often. (3) You become easily upset over little and inconsesquential things. (4) You are on edge most of the time without any apparent reason. (5) You form strange sensitivities. (6) You grow listless or despondent. (7) You "go to pieces" at the slightest provocation. (8) You want to scream or shout imprecations.

(9) You find everything and everybody are in your way. (10) You want to do physical harm to yourself or to others.

If some of these things apply to you, then you are on the verge of a serious mental disturbance. But you may still be able to help yourself in one or more of these ways:

1—Get away from your family and your usual surroundings, where you can relax for a while and take stock of yourself. You may have to dig deep into your feelings and emotions so as to be able to go back and learn how, when, where and why your mental disturbance began.

It may be difficult for you to "put your finger" on all the irritating factors. Yet, some of them may come to light, providing you are sincere in your efforts and seek within yourself or conditions around you. Furthermore, you have to be honest and truthful in your stock-taking and not alibi or justify your contributions to the conditions or circumstances that tend to upset and irritate you.

2—Another way to uncover the basic reasons for a growing mental disturbance is to put things down on paper. Go about it in a methodical manner. Put down all your peeves, annoyances, grievances, resentments and disappointments in detail. No one else is to see what you write, so make it a true exposé. Put down all the details and then evaluate the things you wrote in their true perspective and relationship.

You may learn that one of the reasons why you cannot get along with people is because you are too set in your ways, too rigid in your views or too adamant in your attitudes. You may be expecting too much from your family or others around you and taking yourself too seriously. You may be setting yourself up as a censor or monitor and are too quick to judge people, thus incurring needless resentments. You may be working too hard or are under pressure.

3—Your mental unrest may be due to justifiable worries, because you have undertaken tasks or responsibilities beyond your abilities to handle them well, or because you know you are "riding for a fall" and are doing nothing about it. You hate to "own up" to your inadequacy and are hoping against hope that things will improve. In the meantime you are on edge.

4—Your mental unrest may be due to nervous exhaustion, to overwork, to lack of change or to a vitamin deficiency. A thorough physical examination may be the answer to your troubles. Your doctor may prescribe certain foods or medications and thus help you regain your mental well-being.

5—Your mental unrest may be due to an induced state of mind, to a "build-up" of imaginary situations, to the striving for the impossible, to a rejection of what life offers you, to the mistaken belief that people hate you or shun you, to the nurture of foolish grievanecs or to any resentment bottled up within you. This will eventually reach the explosive stage and turn you into a mental casualty. And, one of the ways to help yourself would be to join a local psychotherapeutic group in its "talk sessions."

There, as one of the small group and under the guidance of the analyst, you will be able to talk freely about the things that trouble you. There, in the open discussions which follow each talk, you may learn how to identify your tensions and how to release your pent-up emotions in harmless ways.

Many of such meetings take place day after day in hundreds of places throughout the country. One or more of them may have weekly or semi-weekly sessions within a short distance from you. The participants are men and women of all ages and in all walks of life. Some of them may be your friends or your neighbors. They are confronted with certain emotional problems and are trying to eliminate the mental hazards involved before such become serious aberrations.

Your local medical board, the psychiatrist's association, the psychological center, the city or county social service agency or senior adult service center know of such "talk sessions" and will put you in touch with the group nearest to you.

However, if you prefer to work out your own problems and offset your growing emotional disturbances through your own efforts, follow some of these steps:

1—Teach yourself to accept your advancing age with all of its inevitable physiological changes.

2—Put to use the things you know best and capitalize upon them.

3—Expose yourself to new contacts and ideas with an open mind and with the readiness to adapt yourself to them.

4—Extend a helping hand to others without turning it into a club, a crutch or an implied obligation.

5—Learn to look for and to derive pleasure and satisfaction from the simple daily things of life.

6—Be willing to "step down" or "step aside" for those younger than you who still have a future to plan for and to work for. Your battles are won and your future is here, now.

7—Welcome the opportunity to give the younger person a lift in whatever way you can, while you take things and life slower, easier.

8—Let no anger or animosity ever linger with you. Dissipate them before they have time to settle. Expose them to ridicule, minimize their effect, disspell their influence and they will not bother you.

9—Stop magnifying your ailments or discomforts. Stop talking about them to strangers or to members of your family. If your pains persist and if your discomforts increase, talk to your doctor and let him take the necessary medical steps to help you.

10—Learn not to confuse normal worry, anxiety, occasional tension or apprehension with emotional disturbances. As an older person, you are bound to have your bad days. You are certain to be upset about something that happened, to resent what someone did or did not do and be disappointed in someone whom you considered wonderful. But whatever they may be, try to treat them lightly. Do not "read into them" and do not ascribe special meanings or importance to them, for they shall surely pass and better moments shall come.

These are some of the ways to cope with minor emotional disturbances. But if you find you cannot help yourself and need outside help, ask your doctor or consult your local health association.

If you can pay for the services to be given, your county medical association, the nearest medical school, or the closest branch of the American Psychiatric Association will provide you with the name of the nearest psychotherapist. If you cannot pay, your county general hospital, your local welfare and service agencies, the old-age assistance offices or the senior citizens service center may help you get the psychiatric help you need.

Do some of these things or let someone else do them for you and soon you will be adding meaning and richness to your golden age.

# CHAPTER FIFTEEN

# How to Acquire Desirable Recreations

The dictionary defines "recreations" and "hobbies" as pleasant, favorite pursuits aside from one's usual interest or occupation. It also gives such synonyms as pastimes, sports, playtime activities, diversions, amusements or relaxations.

All of these words are seemingly interchangeable. But psychologists maintain that insofar as senior adults are concerned, the term "recreation" has a deeper and more purposeful meaning. It implies the selection and the cultivation of one or more leisure time activities to serve not only as a diversion or a relaxation but also as a primary interest. It also applies to activities which could be turned to gainful purposes, to add to one's income if need be, to establish desirable social contacts, to build up one's feeling of self-respect, to promote a sense of self-sufficiency, to generate self-confidence and to provide outlets for self-expression.

These are some of the things that you should look for when you take up given recreations. As a matter of fact, you should cultivate several recreational activities so as to diversify your interests, develop new pursuits, add to your enjoyments and keep you busy doing things. Let the things you

223

take up be pleasant to follow. Let them relax you or refresh you and let them fill your leisure time with enjoyable activities.

Go about those things sensibly with an eye to the future, when your strength or abilities may be somewhat impaired and force you to restrict some of those activities. If you want to study or to learn something new, do not hold back under the mistaken belief that you are too old to learn.

You may find it a little harder to study and to learn new things. You cannot concentrate so wholeheartedly or so readily as a child. Furthermore, you may have to unlearn old habits and old concepts before you are ready to accept the new ideas. This is where a youngster is ahead of you.

On the other hand, as an older adult, you have decided advantages. You have a deeper perception and a better grasp of things. You have a greater capacity to associate or correlate what you learn with what you already know and understand. Hence, if what you are studying interests you and you apply yourself to learning, you will retain a greater amount of what has been taught to you.

Whatever be the things you study or follow up make sure not to take up a given trend, fad or ism, just because it is in current vogue. Do not allow yourself to be influenced by former contacts or former associates just because you are used to them.

Try something different and stay with it only as long as it pleases or satisfies you or brings you a sense of accomplishment. Let it be a change in your usual pace and let it take you out of your usual and customary daily routines.

Of course, it is not easy to give up old habits and preoccupations. You have to go about developing new interests and following new pursuits in a gradual way and eliminate abrupt transitions. You may find the "going" somewhat difficult at first and disheartening even under ideal conditions. So—make allowances for mistakes and do not aim too high.

For instance, if one of your proposed recreations is to learn how to play a musical instrument, select one that is not too difficult to master and be satisfied to play mostly for your own amusement and relaxation. Do not build up false hopes of becoming a concert musician or of gaining fame as a virtuoso. . . . Be content with knowing how to play well enough to be part of a small orchestra or just enough to be able to entertain yourself and your friends.

What are some of the steps to follow in choosing a desirable recreation? Here are several suggestions:

1—Determine beforehand exactly what field or what phase of such field you want to follow.

For instance, if you chose music and the playing of an instrument, select one easy to learn and easy to include in a small "combo" or orchestra. If you used to play a given instrument, try your hand at it again. You may be "rusty," but the old habit will soon reassert itself and within weeks you will be "making music" again to please you and others.

You may want to join a band or an orchestra active in your community but if they cannot use you, why not try to start a small "combo" or orchestra of your own? There may be others like you, who used to play an instrument and would get back to it if someone were to take the initiative to form a new ensemble. The nearest school of music or some of the members of the musician's union in your town may be interested in working with you. Your new group could easily become a wonderful outlet for enjoyment and be a new means of getting together with others as well as a possible source of income for all concerned.

If you chose singing, join the choir at your church, the singers of your club, the chanters of your lodge, or the local choral society. If such a group is not available to you, discuss the matter with others also interested in singing and, perhaps, you could start a new singer's group under your banner. Here, too, you will find that voice teachers and music schools will gladly cooperate.

If you plan to collect records as your hobby, you have a wide variety to choose from, operas, symphonies, instrumental pieces, folk tunes, popular music, and foreign imports. You may decide to specialize in certain artists, countries or periods or go in for collector items. Whatever the case, you may find it rewarding to follow auctions, to visit secondhand stores, to advertise your wants in the local press, and to frequent the thrift shops conducted by your local Goodwill Industries, the Salvation Army, the St. Paul De Vincent Society or the Junior Assistance League, where some of the records you want could be picked up for pennies.

If you have the training or the inclination, you could try to arrange concerts and musicales. You may act as an impresario, on a small scale, and work through booking agencies or an artists' bureau and in conjunction with your local music schools, chamber of commerce and other civic groups bring musical talent into your city.

If you have the knack for it, try your hand at composing or arranging music or teach music to those who cannot afford to pay for it, especially if you are not interested in collecting a fee for teaching. Or, if your finances permit it, underwrite the future of some bright youngster, send him to the proper schools and let him get the training he needs to justify your belief in his ability.

2—Know what the intended activity will demand.

Have a clear understanding of what your proposed recreation will require in time, effort, expense and exertion. Make sure to stay within your means, within the physical energies needed and within the time you can devote to it. For instance, skiing or mountain climbing is definitely out of bounds for you. Boating may be suitable for the time being but sail racing would pose too many hazards and would hardly fit into the recreational activities of an older person.

3—Start on a small scale.

Never undertake any new activity on a large scale. Feel your way at first, especially if it is something new or something which you have not followed for a long time. If it is possible, try to use someone else's equipment or appurtenances for the time being. Do not invest too much money in necessary gear until you are sure the activity is what you want and fits into your future.

The mere fact that you liked to do certain things a few years back is no assurance that you will still find them just as interesting and satisfying. Times and tastes change and many an old interest, like an old love, may be dead. What may have been a delightful all-absorbing pastime years ago could easily be a boring and tedious task for you now.

4—Be the master of your new activity.

Let your new recreation be a helpful, fruitful and restful thing for you and never allow it to become an all-absorbing passion and enslave you.

Some people will "go all out" for playing cards or golf, for attending meetings or following a given sport, for hunting or fishing or becoming involved in various charitable causes. All of these things are good in moderation but not to the exclusion of other desirable activities.

5—Diversify your interests.

Take up several leisure time activities and let them help you find a number of outlets for self-expression, for diversion, for desirable companionships. Join the nearest community center or active Golden Age club where trained professionals can help you gain new interests and learn new things. They may help you uncover hidden talents within you that could add new joys and pleasures to living.

Hobbies and "do-it-yourself" activities are gaining more and more support as many more people want to learn how to do things by themselves, for their own satisfaction and for possible sale to others. Many new manufacturers, wholesalers and retailers are entering the field to cater to and interest hobbyists. There are several periodicals devoted to such interests and in many sections of the country special shows, exhibits and conventions are sponsored to promote and to support the interests of those who take up hobbies for pleasure or satisfaction, for a gainful use of spare time, for ways to supplement one's income or for ways to find relaxation and self-expression.

A recent syndicated special edition of a sixteen-page supplement to the metropolitan Sunday papers featured hundreds of items for the "do-it-yourself" fan and the hobby enthusiast. The listings covered such items as model planes, boats, cars, trains, toys, miniatures, gadgets and what-nots. There was also a special section dealing with tools, patterns, molds, kits, machinery and various assembly units.

In many instances the advertisers offered to supply details and complete instructions on how to make, build, design, assemble or manufacture various items for personal use or for sale to others.

That supplement was only one of the many catalogs, books and pamphlets made available to those who wish to acquire a desirable hobby. Your local librarian or an inquiry to the Superintendent of Documents, U. S. Government Printing Office at Washington, D. C., will give you a long list of material to read and to follow through.

Now, what are some of the "restful," sedentary recreations you could follow that do not call for physical exertions, that do not require special tools or skills, and yet provide you with many hours of interest and enjoyment? Perhaps the "Hobbies of Appreciation" as Dr. Clarence W. Lieb calls them, may give you the right directives. Among them are: (1) The Art of Reading. (2) The Art of Music Appreciation. (3) The Art of Conversation. (4) The Art of Remembering. (5) The Art of Teaching. (6) The Art of Creativeness. (7) The Art of Living With Yourself.

## 1. The Art of Reading

No other field of human interest is so large, so extensive and so absorbing. It embraces the entire range of man's knowledge, thoughts, deeds, fancies and accomplishments. Reading can be a pleasant and rewarding pastime when used sensibly. Some people turn their reading into an escape from life and from themselves. Others make it an opiate and whatever it be that they start reading they must, to their detriment, finish it in one sitting.

Such wanton abuse of one's eyes is harmful. Too much reading at one time without rest periods between leads to eyestrain, to headaches, to tension, insomnia, irritation, distemper and digestive disturbances. No book or magazine is worth that much.

Make the books you read and the periodicals you read, whatever be their contents, your close personal friends and use them in such capacity. Let them open doors for you into the homes and hearts of the writers and the characters portrayed. Let them give you a deeper insight into what makes us love, laugh, hate, live and desire. Let them amuse you without tiring you. Let them teach you the things you want to know. Let them make you think and awaken your imagination. Let them inspire you to do better in whatever way you can. Let them cheer you when you are downhearted and soothe your troubled spirit. Let them lead you in righteous paths and help you be a better parent, neighbor and friend.

Experiment with reading material. For instance, try to read plays which you saw or heard within recent years. Select the plays that held a special appeal to you. Get copies of them at your public library and read them aloud to yourself. Choose some of the characters which you could conceivably portray on the stage or screen, and learn to "read the lines," as if you were auditioning for the part.

Imbue those lines with feeling and try to memorize the most dramatic moments of your part. Make believe that you are the character in real life and give it all the fire, fervor and reality you possibly can. This pretense may lead you to discover hidden talents and open new vistas for you in dramatic art.

Experiment with poetry as another form of reading material. Select descriptive poems by Browning, Keats, Longfellow, Shelley, Whitman or other favorite poets. Read those poems aloud to yourself, in simple recitative style. Follow the soothing, rhythmic, metric cadences without turning your reading into a monotonous sing-song. Stop now and then to ask yourself why the poet chose this or that simile or a given metaphor to depict something, or how he found similarities in dissimilar things. Follow his lead and try to be more descriptive and picturesque in your own conversations. The effort to look for and to use the right word is bound to enrich your vocabulary.

Experiment with nonfictional reading material. Many of the books on history, travel, biography, science, philosophy, psychology and other kindred subjects are written in a simple, easy-to-follow style. You may find them to be good reading and they may add to your knowledge and open new worlds for you.

All of this does not imply that you should put each book on a testing block before you read it, or that you should look askance at short stories and light fiction, but rather that you give yourself a wider scope of choice and turn even occasional reading into an enjoyable pastime.

## 2. The Joys of Music Appreciation

The value of music in any of its forms, as a desirable activity, was elaborated upon in an earlier chapter. Here, however, it is approached from a different aspect, wherein you act not as a participant but as an onlooker, a receptor or a listener.

There is no other form of human communications that holds the same scope, the same impact and impression upon our feelings and emotions which music has. It is truly the "universal language of mankind." To paraphrase Moore: ". . . Even the most effective language is weak, faint and inadequate, before the sweep and the spell of music . . ."

Music is the shortest and quickest way to emphatic response. It is the dynamic projection of sound, rhythm and tempo that transcend time, space, circumstance and personal differeneces. It can be enjoyed by anyone without the need for him to know and to understand the composite elements, because the "feel" for it is the most important factor.

Music impinges upon our sensory centers in three ways at one and the same time: (1) Physiologically, through the sense of hearing. The succession of tonal modulations, of accented rhythmic sounds, of pleasing cadences in set formations, of changing or repetitive tonal combinations build up a tremendous auditory receptivity. (2) Mentally, through the tonal pictures depicted. They span time, joggle memory, awaken dreams, stir the imagination, lift us high above the immediate present and transport us to other scenes and places. (3) Emotionally, by fostering a sense of inner enjoyment, by arousing responsive feelings, by engendering pleasing empathic reactions and by instigating pre-established moods and attitudes.

The opportunities to hear and learn to appreciate music have never been so plentiful as they are nowadays, especially for those who have the time and the desire to listen. With AM and FM radios, with TV musicals, with symphonic concerts offered at popular prices, with stereophonic recordings and home-type tape recorders, the whole world of old and modern music can be yours.

However, the taste for music, especially classics and symphonies, has to be cultivated. But the appellation "classical" does not always or necessarily mean good, enjoyable music, even though it has been given an aura of depth, greatness and mystical meaning by critics and music publishers.

You can develop a better taste and a greater appreciation

for music by following some of the following suggested steps. However, do not take the numerical sequences given as an indication of importance. They are purely accidental.

1—Let your first choice be music with a story, with a definite mood or setting which you can feel or recognize. Overtures may prove to be a good start. Expose your ears to such works as overtures to familiar operas, Aida, Carmen, La Tosca, La Traviata, La Boheme, Madame Butterfly. Or try Mendelssohn's "A Midsummer Night's Dream," Tschaikowsky's "Romeo and Juliet," Smetana's "The Moldau," Brahms' "Academic Festival," Debussy's "The Afternoon of a Faun," to mention but a few of them.

2—Try next to listen to lyrical semi-classical or classical compositions written for one instrument or for an orchestra. Start with serenades, barcaroles, nocturnes, serenatas, tone poems and improvisations on a single theme. Listen carefully and try to absorb as much as you can of each composition without giving it too much thought. Let your taste or "feel" be the deciding factor.

3—Check your personal response to the melody and the overtones, and "let yourself go" even though you do not know and cannot tell the difference between a major and a minor key, between the main melody and the counterpoint in harmony, or how the composer used the various motifs to depict his feelings and interpretations. Let the sounds you hear carry you along for the time being.

4—Move on to symphonies. Start with sonatas or concertos for orchestra and violin. You may like Beethoven's in D Major, Mendelssohn's in E Minor, Brahms' in D Minor. Next try concertos for orchestra and piano, such as Beethoven's No. 5 in E Flat Major, Brahms' No. 2 in B Flat, Tschai-

kowsky No. 2 in B Flat Minor, Rachmaninoff's No. 3 in D
Minor. In orchestral symphonies you may show a greater
preference for Brahms' First, Beethoven's Fifth and Ninth,
Shubert's Ninth, Dworjak's Fifth and Tschaikowsky's Fifth.
You may also find favorites among the works of Berlioz,
Chopin, Mahler, Rachmaninoff and Rimski-Korsakov. All
of these are only a partial list of well-known, highly popular
compositions and no mention was made of such fine com-
posers as Prokofiev, Shustakovitch, Ravel, Stravinsky, Bloch,
Bartok and many others.

5—Be sure to read and acquaint yourself with all the
notes and comments on a given symphonic work as elaborated upon in the catalog, the program or the record envelope
so as to know what the composer had in mind and how he
tried to achieve the desired results through themes, form,
movement, harmony, tempo, counterpoint and tonal interpretations.

6—Listen to each recording, if you bought or rented it,
a number of times. Familiarize yourself first with the high
moments of the composition, where the basic theme is intoned
with bursts of sound, where the grief or the exultation reaches
its highest expression, where the joy or the sadness seems to
overflow its boundaries, when the raging storms subside and
peace or tranquility is restored once again, when all strife is
overcome and love triumphs over all the attendant difficulties.
Then go back to the same composition to find the connecting
links between the basic main melody and its component sup-
porting parts as they are introduced, developed and inter-
mingled.

7—Learn to look for the basic melody and separate it
from the form, rhythm, harmony, contrast, counterpoint and
movements that blend it into a symphonic arrangement. Fol-

low it, no matter how it is manipulated in the composition.
Note especially how the strings or the woodwinds, the brasses
or the percussion instruments join in the ensemble to carry
the melody along or embellish it and thereby create a given
feeling and establish a certain mood of tonal impact.

8—Learn to separate and identify the feelings and reactions which given passages, movements and tonal arrangements engender in you. But do not become all absorbed in
the technicalities used to create the existing feeling or reaction. Let the music flow over you and be concerned only with
how you feel and not why you feel as you do.

9—Look for the personal tie-in between the music and
its effects upon you. Do the tonal cadences seem to soothe
you, to inspire or depress you? Do the tones you hear bring
to life memories of things you want to recall or forget? Do
you enjoy the melody in the form and arrangement used? Is
there a sweep or rhythm or a climax that means something
to you? Ask these and similar questions of yourself, provide
the right answers for them and then guide yourself accordingly.

10—Let your personal feelings about a given musical
composition be the deciding factor. Trust your own likes,
your own judgment and choose only the artists, orchestras
and music you enjoy hearing. You can develop a taste for
better music, you can acquire a greater sense of appreciation
for the blending of themes, you can cultivate a better understanding of the parts which different instruments play in the
presentation of a lengthy and involved symphonic composition. But, your preference should still remain your guide,
and if certain classics or symphonies do not appeal to you,
take them off your favorite lists.

Choose your music as you would a close friend. Then, no matter how many calendar years are added to your age you will enjoy listening to music. Then, music will open new doors for you as it brings cheerful, satisfying tunes to brighten your day.

### 3. The Art of Conversation

Strange as it may sound to you for the moment, there can be a great deal of enjoyment even in ordinary conversations. There is an art to it and you can learn it. Too many people assume that just because they can "mouth" words or because they are emphatic in "speaking their minds," they are good conversationalists.

But such is not the case. There is much more to it. There are certain social amenities to follow, certain prescribed "do's" and "dont's" to observe. You may or may not know them. At any rate, fifteen of them are listed below. Their sequence is incidental and is not to be taken as an indication of their value or importance. Adopt those that will help you and then you will be able to conduct interesting conversations at any time, with a growing enjoyment.

1—Do not "put a period" to whatever you say with the implication that you will brook no dissension, that yours is the one and only way to understand, to interpret and to consider a given situation. That will hardly influence people or make friends for you.

2—Do not assume a "know-it-all" attitude and never underestimate your listeners. One or more of them may be more conversant with the subject matter and may take the notion to "put you in your place," to your considerable embarrassment.

3—Leave room for discussion, for a divergence of opinion. Finish with: "This is the way it looks to me. But what about you? What is your opinion . . .?"

4—Do not monopolize the floor. Give others a chance to speak. Conversation implies a friendly discussion, an informal interchange of views and ideas and not a monologue.

5—Be considerate of the other fellow's rights and sensibilities. Give him the same respect you would expect from him if he were not to agree with what you say.

6—Be slow to "answer back" or the use of abusive language. The words spoken in anger or resentment are seldom right and proper. They can often wreck friendship and good feeling beyond repair.

7—Be selective in the choice of words and descriptions. Avoid the use of old clichés and time-worn phrases. They bespeak a lazy mind and tend to create poor impressions.

8—Do not fall in love with given words or phrases and use them to distraction. Some people form the habit of repeating, ad nauseum, such words as "regardless," "incidentally," "of course," "nevertheless." Or, they repeat such meaningless phrases as "see what I mean," "on the other hand," "believe you me," "do you follow me." Watch for these annoyances and avoid them.

9—Encourage the other fellow to talk about himself, about his pet topics and ideas. He will "love" you for it and consider you the best conversationalist he has ever met.

10—Listen attentively to whatever others say, even if you have to pretend an interest. Then, in turn, they will pay more attention to your comments and opinions.

11—Follow the lead of those who spoke before you if you want to pursue the same trend of thought. Let the comments you make be pertinent enough to keep the same subject matter going.

12—Do not interrupt others even when you must break into the conversation. Give them the right you would expect from them, namely, to complete what they wanted to say, or at least until they come to a pause. Then preface your remarks with: "Will you permit me to inject *this* thought before it slips my mind?" Or, "I'm in accord with you, but may I have your permission to add . . . ?"

13—If people are continually interrupting you, there may be several reasons for it. Perhaps you assume too much or misstate known facts. Perhaps you veer away from the subject matter or repeat yourself to distraction. Perhaps you are too officious or dogmatic, too imperious or opinionated, and your listeners resent it.

14—Be tactful and diplomatic even when those around you are rude and uncouth. Let your conversation and your manner bespeak amenity and fairmindedness. And, if you have to criticize someone never do it in the presence of others.

15—Be quick with your compliments and find something good to say about those who participate in your general conversation. They will like it and try to be pleasant in your presence. This will add to your enjoyments.

Follow some of these suggestions when you are among others and soon even a casual conversation will become a meaningful and pleasant recreation for you.

### 4. The Art of Remembering

Strange as it may sound, you can cultivate the art of remembering and turn it into an absorbing recreation, one that would be available to you at a moment's notice, regardless of time, place or circumstance.

The artist and the teller of tales have developed the ability to recall into a fine, profitable activity. They learned how to see with their eyes closed, how to listen without hearing a sound and how to depict what they see and hear in striking, picturesque ways. They learned to see with the inner eye and to listen with their minds and their hearts.

You can follow in their steps, even now, at your present age. Start by developing your sense of observation. Get into the habit of looking at something and really seeing it. Then close your eyes and try to re-create in your mind's eye what you saw, in all of its details.

Make your initial start with your living room. You have seen it hundreds of times and should be familiar with everything about it, but it is safe to say that you are not. For instance, can you tell how big it is, in square feet? How large are the windows? What type of windows are they? How many panes are there to each window? How far is each window sill from the floor and the ceiling? If there are draperies, what is the size of each panel and what are the color combinations? What kind of rug is on the floor? What is the pattern and the color scheme? Could you make a rough sketch of the design or describe it in detail? If there are pictures on the walls, who painted them? What are the dimensions of each picture? What does each picture depict? Can you describe the various pieces of furniture in the room, as to style, size, period, wood finish and other details? Put your answers down on paper and then make the comparison. You will be entitled to commendation if you are fifty per cent right. So—make this test now and see how well you see.

Now, try this idea. Notice carefully the next stranger you meet. Give him your undivided attention for fifty or sixty seconds without making it obvious, then walk away and try to list on paper all the things you can remember about him. There are over one hundred distinctive differences between one person and another. How many could you list about the stranger?

Start with his general appearance, with his apparent age, height, weight and build. Go on to his complexion, to his facial features, to the shape of his head, the contour of the face, the hairline, the color of hair and the way it is cut or worn; the temples, ears, forehead, eyes, eyebrows, nose, shape of nares, the upper lip, the lower lip, the chin, neck and the profile.

Try to recall his voice, its intonations and inflections, and whether or not his speech had a localized twang or an accent. Describe the clothes he wore, his posture and his mannerisms; recall the shape of the hands, the fingers and the rings he wore, if any. Put down your impression as to his background, his line of work or profession. Was there something about him that impressed you? How? Why? Was it in the way he spoke, walked or held himself? Did he remind you of someone you know, of someone you like or dislike? What were the differences or the similarities?

Is that asking too much of you? If so, try to describe along these lines someone you have met a number of times, at work or at play. Do this several times and soon you will see better. . . .

Have you ever tried to describe a musical composition? This is how one writer gave a word picture of a piano solo:

"They were alone in the room. She remained near the open window. He walked over to the piano, sat down and let his fingers touch the keys softly, caressingly. He flicked several soft glissandos, toying with their rippling sound, added several basso chords and sustained them with quickly rising crescendos. His eyes sought her face and caught a fleeting smile. He started a melody. It was simple and plaintive at first, with a sorrowful undertone, as if echoing his regrets of the years he lost without her. He changed the melody into a repetitive rhythmic refrain. It advanced and receeded with a consistent recurring beat as if voicing and repeating his plea for her love.

"Then his fingers began to move freely, quickly, over the keyboard. His playing became a bantering, challenging cadence. The melody was now gay, joyful, lilting, confident, yet delicate and sweet, tender and cajoling. Soon the tempo gathered speed and the melody changed into a spirited dance, triumphant, exuberant, as if his search for her love was over. His fingers moved faster and faster, the tones grew boastful, arrogant in rollicking cadenzas, then came to a sudden stop with the roar and the crash of double chords . . ." Does this description paint a vivid word picture for you? Could you do as well in describing something you saw or heard? Perhaps not, but would it not be fun to try?

To paraphrase a passage from *How to Conquer Fears, Worries and Frustrations in 30 Hours*, ". . . You do not have to be a poet or a painter, a student or a scholar, an artist or a writer to be able to see, hear, look, listen, enjoy and appreciate the beauty, the majesty and the absorbing intensity of life within you and all around you. . . . Nature in its myriad forms, beginning with you, is teeming with sights and sounds, with motion and action. Just open your eyes and learn to see, open your ears and learn to listen, open your heart and let it bring the world to you . . ."

One of the ways to learn how to do these things, whoever you are and wherever you may be, is to cultivate the art of remembering. Begin to put into the vaults of your memory all the pleasant and desirable things you want to remember. It is not too late. Begin with your immediate sensations and impressions. Begin to accumulate the scenes and sights, the sounds and the scents you would like to keep for future use. Add them to the other memorable happenings already put away and make them available to yourself whenever gloom or sorrow comes your way.

Establish a library of color. Impress upon the tablets of your memory, in all of their radiant hues and tints, the colorful animate and inanimate life around you. Etch deeply the bright yellows, the graduating pinks and the flaming reds of the setting sun. Imprint upon your memory the serenity and the solemnity of the night, as the silvery moon glides across a cloudless sky or as the twinkling stars overhead bespeak the infinity of space. Engrave upon the tablets of your memory the beauty of the sunrise as its brightening yellows and radiant reds drive away the purple shadows of the night and herald the coming of a new, virgin day. Give room in the files of your memory to the beauty of each newborn day as the seasons of the year change from the lush greens of spring to the vivid colors of summer, from the golden browns of the autumn to the pristine whiteness of the newly fallen winter snow.

Build up your treasure troves of sound. Imprint upon your memory the fragile peep-peep of a frightened fledgling, the eerie whistling of the wind, the rhythmic patter of rain, the soothing refrain of a lullaby, the carefree laughter of a child, the haunting strains of a love song, the becalming tonal

cadence of a hymn or the harmonious comingling of the instruments in a symphony.

Refurbish the treasure troves of the nice and enjoyable
things life brought to you through the years. Reclassify and
revivify the memorable things you learned from others, the
good books you read, the inspiring plays you saw and heard,
the paintings and other works of art which you admired, the
ennobling thoughts you gained through spiritual exaltation
and all the commendable acts you did through the years, out
of the goodness of your heart. Recall at leisure all those occa-
sions when you were kind, considerate, loyal, unselfish; when
you extended help to others freely, gladly, and earned their
heartfelt thanks.

These treasure troves of memory are yours to hold. No
keys can ever be made to open them without your consent and
no power on earth can ever change their contents. You, and
you alone, can enter the vaults at any time desired and use
them as much and as often as you please without ever deplet-
ing the contents. What is more, you can add hundreds and
thousands of additional items without ever overloading the
vaults or affecting the original contents in any way.

And here is the strangest part of all. The more you dip
into the vaults of your memory the easier it becomes to take
things out, and the more you share the contents with others
the more you have to share and enjoy.

What are the best ways to dip into your memory and bring
to life the things you want to enjoy once again? There are
no special ways. At the beginning it may be necessary for
you to be away from people and noise so that you commune
with yourself and be able to send memory back into the past,
to the particular sights, scenes, sounds or incidents you wish
to recall.

Later on, when you developed the ability to hold your mind in concentrated thought, you will be able to retreat to the privacy of your own mind and enjoy, even in the midst of a crowd, the treasure troves of your memory. Yes, with the proper discipline you can teach your mind to obey and thus learn how to retire into yourself and there "keep with perfect sweetness the independence of your solitude."

Learn to put to good use the treasure troves of your memory for your own pleasure, for no matter how many years passed or how many changes took place since the initial memory deposit you can span time and space and circumstance in split seconds and re-create all those pleasant happenings in all of their desirable and enjoyable details.

Learn to put to good use the treasure troves of your memory to help others in their moments of need, when they need to be encouraged and could lean on you with trust and confidence. You may have been in similar situations and found a way out. By citing your experiences and telling others how you weathered the sad or bad times, they, too, may learn how to meet their immediate problems.

This readiness on your part to utilize your memory files for your own pleasure and to help others can become a rewarding recreation. Be sure, however, to keep memory under control and do not let it fill you with needless regrets about what could have been and might have been. Avoid the tendency to live in the past or to seek ways to return to it. Live to the most now, and let memory sweeten and enrich the present moment. Then, and only then, will memory serve you well and become a desirable recreation for your golden age. It will take a little practice to keep memory in line but the effort will repay you in a thousand ways.

## 5. *The Art of Teaching*

Even though you never had professional training and never gave a single lesson to anyone you can find considerable satisfaction and enjoyment now to teach others how to do some of the things you know well.

For instance, as a man who was active in a given field, held an executive position or followed a certain profession, there may be dozens of ways in which you can tell or teach younger men and women in the same field how to solve minor problems and overcome certain difficulties.

As a mother, a wife, a homemaker, you faced problems in the past with your children, with in-laws, with your husband, with neighbors, with sickness, with reverses and difficulties. Now, in the light of your experiences you may be able to tell others how to meet and resolve similar situations.

As a matured man or woman willing to serve your community, you could join others to teach or to counsel youth in the ways of life. You may be a good influence on teenagers or want to serve as a liaison between juvenile delinquents and the law or correctional institutions. You may have the knack to handle the mentally retarted, the sick, the aged, or those who need rehabilitation.

As a matured man or woman with an open mind, you may find considerable satisfaction in working with interracial groups and help to establish closer amicable relationships between races, creeds and minorities in your community. This holds tremendous possibilities to work in God's way and help make this world of ours a better place in which all peoples can live peacably together.

As a retired man who acquired certain skills, in working with your hands, with tools or equipment, you may have something valuable to offer in classrooms. There is hardly a school principal anywhere who would not welcome your service along such lines, even if you do not have a college degree or regular teaching credentials.

For instance, one man who was a conductor on a cross-country passenger train most of his life decided to relate his experiences of early-day travel across the country while the West was still wild and perilous. His tales of those days enthralled the classes in history and in geography and made them "red-letter" days in the lives of the children.

Another man, a former tool and die maker, gives practical lessons in handling precision tools to trade classes at two high schools in his town. He supplements them with private tutoring at his home where he fitted out the garage into a small machine shop.

One woman with time on her hands who is especially good in baking pies and preserving fruit, decided to impart some of her knowledge to youngsters at school. Her offer was quickly accepted and her hours at the home economics classes at the local high school and junior college are among the most popular.

The four cases picked at random barely scratch the surface of how much you could do and how good you might be as a teacher. Ask yourself, what is it that I know or that I can do which could be imparted to others? No matter what it is, if you can explain it in simple words so that anyone could understand, if you can show how it is done in ways that others could follow you, then you can surely teach, even if you never taught school for a single hour.

Talk things over with one or more school principals in your neighborhood or in your town. Tell him about the things you did and know. This may well start you on a new road to better and happier days in your golden age.

## 6. The Art of Creativeness

The desire to create something of your own is strong in every human heart. Some of us let our creative urge die, others work at it until some satisfaction is gained. Some need the time or the push, the opportunity or the will power to achieve their heart's desire. Others will overcome all obstacles and will rise from simple humble beginnings to gain fame and renown, seemingly against impossible odds and handicaps.

What makes one child a genius and another born into the same family and under the same circumstances just an ordinary youngster? Geneticists have a ready answer for it. They contend that you are the composite of all your parental and maternal ancestors, that among the millions of genes and chromosomes passed on to you by your parents, every trait, attribute, tendency and ability of your ancestors are present. As such, you have thousands of ancestors to draw from and if the genes of one of your gifted predecessors are predominant in you, you could conceivably become the recorder and the transmitter of those talents.

The geneticists go on to say that although you may know your parents, your four grandparents and perhaps even one of your eight great-grandparents, you had thirty-two of them in five generations. But if you were to trace your family tree back only another one hundred years, a total of ten generations, you would have one thousand and thirty-two ancestors. Yes, 1,032 men and women who contributed to your make-up, your thoughts, personality, abilities, tendencies and special propensities.

So—it is highly possible that deep within you are many untold potentialities. Perhaps all they need to come forth is a gentle nudge from you or from someone else. The indications may be noticeable in what interests you most. If you know what it is, well and good. But if you are not sure, then you may have to try your hand at several things.

You may decide to try painting. It is a tremendous field. You have your choice of subject matter, of animate or inanimate life, of real or imaginary subjects, or different backgrounds and perspectives, of variations in lights and shadows, with all the colors of the spectrum at your disposal. You can use the primary function of color as an emotion or a structure, as a complement or a decoration. Your subjects can be of any type or nature to suit you. You can dip into history or religion, into domestic or romantic life, into still life or portraits, into seascapes or landscapes, into architectural drawings or imaginative fancies.

The process you select for painting can be oil or ink, fresco or tempera, crayon or charcoal, enamel or water colors. And your painting could be done on paper or canvas, on wood or cardboard, on walls or ceilings, on stone or tile, on glass or on porcelain.

On the other hand, you may decide to follow paintings only as a collector, as a student or an observer. There, too, you have a tremendous field from which to choose, and your local art schools, museums and public library can help you follow such pastime. For instance, you may decide to trace the art of painting from the primitive cave drawings to the cubistic and surrealistic examples of our times. Yet, at the same time, you could pause anywhere along the route or wander off onto side roads to concentrate on given periods, on certain artists, on given subjects or on certain schools of painting, to suit your wishes and inclinations.

You may decide to take up clay modeling because it has special fascinations. It provides you with the means to fashion something with every movement of your fingers and to change the shape, size or form of what you are making by kneading, cutting, adding, pressing or manipulating the clay to suit your sudden whim. This promotes a feeling of importance, a sense of accomplishment, and at the same time tends to soothe and relax you.

You may decide to take up etching in metal, carving in wood, tooling in leather, working with plastics, making rugs or becoming a "master" in contract bridge. You may decide to go back to school to complete the education you missed or to take up a given subject merely for the sake of the satisfaction it would bring you as a student in that field.

You may decide to do something seemingly foolish such as writing the words for a popular song and composing the music for it. You do not have to be a poet or a musician to try your hand at it, because even if you do not know one note from another, you can hum or sing your melody onto the tape of an inexpensive tape recorder and then have a music arranger transfer the melody on paper.

One form of song writing which is fairly easy and which could provide you and your friends with many amusing moments would be to write parodies for old-time songs. It is not so difficult if you have a sense of humor, an imaginative flair, a feeling for rhyming and know the rudiments of metrical cadence.

Take any one of the old-time favorites. Use the present lyrics as your guide and substitute other lines in the same rhyme sequence. Let it be in the jocular, the humorous, the whimsical or nonsensical vein. Make sure, however, to retain the same beat, tempo and syllabic cadence.

For instance, suppose you were to try parodizing the popular old-time favorite, "Home On the Range." You will note that the first two lines rhyme "home" with "roam." The beat is 1-2-2; 1-2-3. "Oh/give me/a home; Where/the buff/-alo roam."

Your parody could take up one of these trends of thought: "Oh, give me a beer that is mel-low and clear . . ." Or, "If you were a Miss and I asked for a kiss . . ." Or, "Oh, give me a meal that to me will appeal . . ." Or, "Oh, give me a friend who can understand . . ." Or, "I don't feel blue when I am with you . . ." These are just a few parody ideas you could use to write new lyrics for "Home On the Range" and thus get a real "bang" from it.

You may not be able to do it on the spur of the moment and may have to try again and again to get the necessary meter. But by keeping at it, especially if you have a feeling for rhyming, or else buy a rhyming dictionary, you will eventually have passable lyrics and gradually emerge as a parodist, to your own satisfaction and to the amusement of your family and friends. At any rate, it is worth a try.

Here is how one amusing parody was built around the old familiar song, "Ain't She Sweet."

> Ain't she fat, waddling toward me,
> Now I ask you very confidentially,
> Ain't she fat.
> Ain't she big, like a tub rollin' down to sea,
> Now I ask you very confidentially,
> Ain't she big.

Just cast an eye in her direction,
Oh me! Oh my! An el'phant in reflection.
Now you can see, why with her I hate to be,
Let me ask you very confidentially,
Can you blame me?

Perhaps you would like to write stories. Then why not try it? What if you do not write the best story of the year? What if it is not accepted for publication? The mere effort to plan and to visualize different characters and situations may bring you a sense of well-being and accomplishment. Perhaps you would prefer to write stories for children? They could be fairy tales or true happenings adapted to the knowledge and concepts of children.

Perhaps you would like to chronicle dramatic events in your life and the lives of others around you, tying them in with national and international happenings, in a semi-historical autobiographical form. You may do it purely for your own pleasure and relive your life, as it were, or do it for the value such chronological account may have for your family as well as for others.

You could follow your urge to write by starting a correspondence with people of your own age or younger than you, in foreign lands. Thus, as a pen pal you will be exchanging news and have enjoyable visits with others, thousands of miles away. Your church, the foreign trade department of your local chamber of commerce, the overseas welfare agencies and the consulate offices of countries in which you are interested will be glad to put you in touch with one or more pen pals or tell you how to go about it.

And, if you have the financial means and no obligations to someone at home, you could expand your contacts with your pen pals into something more substantial. You might undertake to become the foster parent of a youngster in some far-off place and take a hand in shaping his or her future.

## 7. *The Art of Living With Yourself*

Offhand you may scoff at the idea that there is an art to living. Strangely enough, there is, and the better you know and understand yourself the easier and the happier your life.

To paraphrase passages from *How to Conquer Fears, Worries and Frustrations in 30 Hours:* "You are the mirror that reflects everything within you and around you. . . . The reflection is the sum total of your knowledge, experiences, opinions, beliefs and prejudices. . . . You can be your own worst enemy or best friend. It is in how you use or abuse your senses, organs and nervous system. It is in how you think, act, feel, behave and respond. It is in how you accept and interpret ideas and concepts. It is in how you follow or disregard the dictates of common sense and the promptings of your heart. . . ."

You have been living with your body and with your mind all your life and have been taking many things for granted. Now, with time on your hands, why not learn a little about what makes you act and react as you do? There is so much to learn, so much to know, and what vistas those things would open for you!

For instance, what do you know about your heart or your bone structure or the marvelous circulating system of your blood? What is the function of your liver? What important tasks are entrusted to your kidneys? How do you breathe? How does your body maintain its normal temperature? How do you see, hear, taste or smell? How is the food you eat converted into body energy?

What is the aging process? What brings you to tears? What makes you laugh, and why? Why do you like or dislike certain things? In what ways do you differ from your spouse or other members of your family? What pleases you or annoys you most? Can you tell why? What makes you feel as you do about certain people? If you have certain beliefs or convictions, how did they form? How would you rate yourself as a parent, a neighbor, a friend?

These are just a few of the questions you can ask of yourself and there are answers for them in books, magazines and in classes which you could attend. Learn some of these things and you will have a better understanding of your feelings and emotions. Adapt some of these things to your daily life and you will learn the art of living better with yourself and with others.

This chapter barely touched all the avenues open to you to find new recreations, to enlarge your interests and to enrich your life. There are so many things to do, so many ways to grow, if you but open your eyes, your ears, your mind and your heart. So—give yourself room to learn and to know and to mellow with your years. Then, whatever be the recreations you take up they will surely add to the richness of your days and make you GLAD you are growing older.

CHAPTER SIXTEEN

# How to Propose Favorable Legislation

What are the proposals you should sponsor on a county, state and national level? What are some of the things you have the right to demand from the local and the Federal government? What are the steps you, and others like you, can take to secure the help you need to retain your physical and mental well-being and be able to maintain a decent, adequate, satisfactory standard of living?

The growth of America, the prominence it attained, the high standards of living we enjoy and the prestige we have in the world at large did not come by accident. It is the result of work, of planning and growing, and you were a part of it. To be sure, the ingenuity, the daring, the resourcefulness, the driving force of men of vision and adequate financial support played a major role. But you, and millions of others like you, contributed heavily of your sweat and toil, of care and effort, of loyalty and dependability, through your working years, to make all of these things possible.

Now, having reached your older age, in enforced retirement from work, you should not be penalized and made to live in reduced circumstances because you do not have the money to pay for decent housing, for proper medical care, for good food and for all the things so essential to dignified living.

You are entitled to certain privileges and allowances in housing facilities, in medical help and in direct financial assistance. The land which benefited by your labors through the years owes something to you. It is a debt, an obligation, which the people of this land, through its legislative and executive branches of government, cannot and must not ignore.

Offhand, this trend of thought may sound radical. It could be branded as a fantastic scheme for the old to sponge on the young, as a crazy idea to make the states and the Federal government become the "Lady Bountiful" for the benefit of the older citizens. But, is this idea so strange, so outlandish? Compare it with the many special subsidies, allowances, concessions, grants and all the other outright gifts being made right now to various domestic groups and foreign lands.

Here are a few of them:

Item 1. Under the National Security Act, the Foreign Aid Program, or under some other equally high-sounding name, we are giving away billions of dollars a year to other nations. These huge appropriations are intended to stabilize the economy of such nations, to strengthen their defenses, to counteract possible subversive activities within their borders and to encourage favorable-to-us relations.

Item 2. We spend billions of dollars a year at home in road building, in highways, in waterways, in dams, in reforestation plans, in various state-wide, Federally supported projects in given areas. These are intended to make things easier and life more comfortable for workers, farmers, home owners, ranchers, businesses and numerous commercial enterprises. We do it as a matter of policy.

Item 3. We release churches, religious orders, charitable bodies and various nonprofit organizations from the payment of property taxes and thereby make special allowances to them on a local and national level.

Item 4. We make special income tax allowances and other concessions for the blind and take care of the mentally deficient or the mentally sick, providing them with food, shelter and medical care.

Item 5. We provide financial and medical care and in many cases pay all of their living costs for the poor and the indigent of all ages, and often bend backwards to give them the help they need, even in such cases where some of them could become self-supporting with proper rehabilitation methods.

Item 6. We spend billions of dollars a year for the good of children. School is a "must" for all youngsters from age five to sixteen or eighteen.

Item 7. We protect the wheat and the potato crops, the cotton grower, the milk and butter producers and many other farm interests, under the parity bill, by paying them money NOT to plant and NOT to produce. Then we sink billions of dollars in the stockpiling of surplus items and various farm products already produced or processed.

Item 8. We protect the oil and mining interests, under the 27% depletion clause, in their income tax returns, and thereby give them millions of dollars a year in "depletion" allowances.

Item 9. We pay for the schooling of veterans, under the GI Bill, and subsidize them during their learning period, in addition to other allowances and exemptions given them on a local, state and national level.

Item 10. We underwrite the expansion of many commercial and industrial firms that work on government contracts. They are allowed to write off their entire investment in equipment, in machinery, in material and in buildings within a few years, and thus the companies are presented with millions of dollars a year in income tax reductions and deductions.

If such grants, concessions, allowances, exemptions and outright gifts can be made with full public approval under Federally instituted enactments, then the senior citizens of the land, who contributed to the wealth of the nation and made such expenditures possible, are also entitled to needed Federal assistance.

This is a direct challenge to all civic-minded citizens and legislative bodies in the land as well as to the men and women elected to respective legislative and executive offices, who must not forget the needs of the aged. It is also a challenge to you, and to the millions of others like you, who should insist that proper steps be taken to make life easier for you.

What ARE some of the things you can ask to be legislated in your favor? What ARE some of your rights? Here are a few of them:

1—Your inalienable right to grow old in peace, in the dignity of your matured age, without apologies to anyone because you are no longer steadily employed or because you have to take life slower and easier. Your status as a human being, as a parent or a neighbor, as a voter and a taxpayer, as a resident and a member of a given community, has not changed because industry and commerce decreed that at 65 you had to be retired and "put out to pasture."

The calendar years of your age have no direct bearing upon your ability to think, to plan, to live, to work and to be productive. Some people reach their old age in their forties, while others seem to gain their second wind in their late sixties and seventies and thus become more valuable to themselves and to others.

2—Your indisputable right to be looked upon and be treated as a mature, independent adult who does not wish to be coddled because of his age or be pushed aside as an "old-ster" and a "has-been." Too many younger adults maintain the mistaken notion that age 65 is the end of the road, that when anyone passes his 65th birthday he immediately loses his abilities to work, to think or to act in a judicious manner.

Of course, there are many older men and women who are sick, who are beset with degenerative chronic diseases, who are senile or bedridden and need constant specialized care. But old age in itself is not the sign of debility any more than youth is the assurance of good health. There are literally thousands of young men and women and even children who are sick or crippled, bedridden or mentally ill and who shall never lead normal self-sustaining lives.

On the other hand, a large percentage of adults past 65, roughly about 66%, retain their health and their faculties. They can, and many of them would welcome it, continue to work and be useful in their respective fields. In many instances there is very little loss in their productive capacity. As a matter of record, in some cases, their training, knowledge, experience, skill and matured judgment become more valuable to all concerned.

3—Your unquestionable right to have a mind of your own, to make your own decisions, to use your own judgment in matters pertaining to your conduct and your interests. You want the right to "run your own life," without censure or recriminations from your children or friends and without interference from well-meaning but often badly placed admonitions from welfare agency personnel.

You may ask for help to find something useful and desirable to do. You may need assistance to secure decent housing accommodations within the limitations of your budget. You may want help to maintain a fair, decent standard of living. But you do not want pity, patronage, regimentation or "handouts." You feel that you are entitled to be heard and at the same time be given the opportunity to exercise your initiative in doing and in following the things you like to do and the things you can do.

4—Your irrefutable right to seek self-improvement and self-expression on your own terms. You are old enough to know your own mind and you prefer to follow your likes and preferences even when they appear childish in the eyes of your children, in the opinions of your friends and in the beliefs of social service and welfare agencies.

Of course, you will make mistakes now and then, try to do more than you should or go off at a tangent. But somehow, you prefer it, even when you have to suffer for lapses to iron-clad restrictions or regimentation. You want the chance to prove to yourself, if to no one else, that you can still work at something. You also want to cope with some of life's problems as you retain your self-independence.

Above all, you do not wish to be told over and over again that you are too old to work or too old to learn something new, too old to go on trips or too old to marry again, too old to select your own diversion or too old to have a mind of your own.

5—Your indisputable right to look for and find fun,

pleasure and relaxation on your own, in keeping with your particular wishes and inclinations. This assumes, of course, that you know your way, know what you can do, are sensible about it and can truly "follow through."

Age may have dimmed your eyes and affected your hearing but glasses can be fitted and hearing aids can be bought. Even if other infirmities plague you from time to time, you still have the urge and the desire to mingle with people, to acquire new interests, to make new friends, and to take part, on a restricted basis, in life around you.

6—Your incontestable right to go places, to meet people in different walks of life and to associate with members of the opposite sex. Your children and others may color such association with abnormal sexual urges and amoral overtones and in some cases may have justifiable reasons for their assumptions. But, as a rule, and this applies to the largest majority, the average older person is sane and sensible and is not swayed so readily by sexual urges and amoral cravings.

Most older adults treat their association with members of the opposite sex as a companionship. At times it is only the wish to share ideas and experiences, to talk with someone, to go on trips or to shows with a congenial companion.

7—Your inferable right to seek full or part-time employment, either to supplement your income or to have extra money for luxuries, without having to give an account to anyone who may claim jurisdiction over you. Of course, your health or your infirmities may keep you from working at something you know and there may be need for vocational rehabilitation. However, you want to retain the right to choose rehabilitation training in keeping with your interests and inclinations.

8—Your unimputable right to stay well and to maintain your physical and mental well-being as long as possible. You feel, therefore, that you are entitled to the best that modern science and medical skill offers. You have no way of telling how long you will live, but you want to stay as healthy as you can be within the limitations of your age and existing infirmities.

So—if illness or disease, if organic or nervous disorders come your way, you want all the help needed without having to beg or fight for it. You want preventive as well as palliative help. You want it not as a dole or charity but as a debt due you for all the years YOU gave to help make America one of the richest and greatest nations in the world.

9—Your indivertible right to ask for suitable meeting places and recreation centers, with proper facilities indoors and outdoors, built in convenient, readily accessible locations, with your needs and physical limitations in mind. Such meeting places to be made available to you, and to others like you, at the hours and times most desirable and convenient for you.

10—Your unchallenged right to be able to attend classes for adults at established schools without the usually required prerequisites. And, if you do not have the money to pay, to have those classes made available to you at no tuition fees. Furthermore, you also want the right to ask for special courses geared particularly to your needs or desires, provided that a sufficient number of other adults seek the same knowledge and can join you in such educational activity.

11—Your inalterable right to ask for a realignment of pensions, old-age assistance, social security benefits or other subsidies paid to you to enable you to meet the rise in living costs and your growing needs for medical care and services.

Such adjustment to be automatic, as part of a Federal plan, applicable to all states and areas, so that wherever you might be you will receive the extra funds needed. The procedure to be copied from the practices now in use in labor contracts.

12—Your immutable right to receive detailed, simplified information on diet and nutrition, especially as applied to your needs as an older person, and to know all the latest measures used to correct poor nutritional habits. All of this to be furnished to you without charge and as often as new facts and findings are released to mercantile channels and to the medical profession.

13—Your undeniable right to receive special allowances from public transportation companies, similar to discounts given to members of the clergy, as you travel on trains, buses, streetcars and other public conveyances. What is more, you believe that you are entitled to a special discount on drugs and pharmaceutical supplies, as well as a tax exemption on real and personal property owned and used by you.

14—Your inviolate right to receive psychological and psychiatric help, at little or no cost, if you are in need of such services and cannot pay for them. This should be available to you under some form of Federal subsidy no matter where you happen to live.

15—Your incontrovertible right to ask for and to receive professional help from people trained in gerontology and old-age counseling. They should be available to you as guides, counselors, group leaders and program chairmen, to make things easier for you and others like you.

This may seem like an overly ambitious program to ask for, but it would not involve too much in the actual outlays

of money. Well, what can you do to instigate and carry
through the enactment of such legislation?

Here are a few suggestions:

Join forces with other men and women in your age group
to form an organization to gain status as such and to be able
to voice your wishes.

Take an active part in the proceedings of such group and
let it become affiliated with other similar groups on a city,
county, state and national level.

Let your voices be heard and your wishes made known to
the men and women in office who represent you in the executive and legislative branches of your city, county, state and
Federal government.

Encourage and support candidates for various offices who
know your problems, who consider your needs, who will take
up your cause and who will instigate legislation in your
behalf.

Demand from all men and women running for office a
clear and direct statement on issues pertaining to your welfare
and then keep track on what they propose and how they vote
on such issues after they have been elected to office.

Insist that the officials you helped to office live up to the
promises made at election time. Make your displeasure known
to them when they fail to follow through and then use the
power of your vote to remove them from office.

Remain alert to various bills being introduced in your
city, county, state or at Washington, D. C. Be quick to support
those in your favor and just as quick to voice your objections
to those inimical to your welfare.

Become acquainted with the aims and objectives of the
various associations of retirees and senior adults. Get the

details of what you and your group would gain by a membership in one of these national associations: the National League of Senior Citizens, 1031 So. Grand Ave., Los Angeles 17, Calif.; the American Society for the Aged, 590 Fifth Ave., New York 36, N. Y.; the Senior Social Service of America, 704 So. Spring St., Los Angeles 14, Calif.; the Senior Citizens of America, 1129 Vermont Ave. N.W., Washington 5, D. C.; the American Association of Retired Person, 310 East Grand Ave., Ojai, Calif.

There are a number of other groups, societies and associations on a city, county, state and national level that work for and with older adults throughout the country. Make inquiries in your own community and be ready to work with others for your common good.

Then, there shall be power in your voice, strength in your efforts, and meaning in your objectives. Then, you shall have a better chance to make your life brighter, sweeter and happier in your golden age.

# CHAPTER SEVENTEEN

# A Manual to Better Speeches

Are you the leader or the organizer of a senior adult group? Would you like to give talks to them or are you the program chairman who has to arrange speakers? Whatever the case, this condensed manual for speakers before older adults may help you.

To adapt the manual more easily to your needs, the various aspects of the subject matter are subdivided as follows: (1) The general problems of the aging person. (2) The tasks of a given speaker. (3) The interests of senior adults. (4) Guideposts for speakers before senior adults. (5) How to treat a senior adults audience. (6) How to deal with self-improvement topics. (7) How the speaker can tie in extraneous material. (8) How a speaker can enhance the value of his speeches. (9) How he can encourage audience participation. (10) How to secure suitable speakers from local sources. The material as given is highly condensed and you are urged to supplement it through books available at your public library.

### 1. The General Problems of the Aging Listener

You may be well adjusted to your age and environment and be fully aware of your needs and your problems. If so, you are indeed fortunate because most people, especially those who retired recently from work, are not prepared to enjoy their leisure hours.

In the case of a man who was active during all his working years, retirement comes as a shock unless he prepared himself for it. Otherwise, the sudden break in old habits and procedures is too sharp, too disturbing. It is even more aggravating when he is in apparent good health, when he does not feel older or less capable to follow his former work, and he deeply resents the enforced retirement.

He is left with idle hands and too much time. He does not know what to do with himself. He does not know how to fill the long, empty hours, day after day. He starts to brood or becomes preoccupied with himself or begins to meddle in the lives of his family and his neighbors. Or else he decides to prove to others that he can still do things, make money, be important, and falls prey to bunco artists, to confidence men or designing women.

The sad aftermaths of such experiences are nurtured later into deep resentments. They turn into frustrations or complexes, foster psychomatic ailments and often lead to serious mental disturbances.

In the case of a woman who reached old age and lost her husband along the way, and the number of widows is growing each year, her future holds little promise of comfort, interest, love or enjoyment. In her desperation she begins to meddle in the affairs of her children or in the lives of her friends. It leads to needless quarrels, to misunderstandings and to eventual estrangements.

With those avenues closed to them, some women turn to cults or fads; others grow self-centered or unduly preoccupied with their faces and figures. Some turn into dyspeptics, into chronic complainers or hypochondriacs, while still others try to push time back. They form misalliances, seek attention or romance in the most unlikely places and fall easy prey to schemers and adventurers.

All of this is further aggravated by the physical manifestations of advancing age, by growing infirmities, by the gradual impairment of the senses, by poorer sleep, and by the initial onslaught of degenerative diseases. Some of the aging persons take those inevitable changes in their stride. Others fight them all the way. Those who fight time either withdraw into themselves or grow despondent, develop anti-social tendencies or contemplate suicide. Others become abusive or defiant, cranky or autocratic, demanding or officious, and thus are a source of constant irritation to themselves and to others around them.

Many an older person often feels rejected. Instead of being one of the doers and active participants, he is pushed into a corner or stays on the outside. He is ignored by old associates, repulsed by the younger members of his family and looked upon as an interloper. He needs new concepts of his "place in the sun" and needs reassurance of his values to someone. He needs guidance and sympathy, encouragement and understanding.

Many an older person who is not kept busy at something has too much time to himself. He begins to pay more and more attention to his little pains or discomforts and becomes sensitized to the telltale marks of his advancing years. He resents the need to be more careful about food, drink, sleep. He resents the necessity to curb some of his old established habits in doing things and going places. He resents the fact that he IS growing old and coming closer to the end. He needs a realistic reappraisal of his daily life and new attitudes toward himself and the world around him.

Many an older person with too much idle time on his hands grows increasingly aware of what is happening to others in his age group. Friends, neighbors, former associates and relatives take sick, grow infirm or die, and he begins to dread the coming day. He needs something to take his mind off himself, something to keep him busy and active and more self-assuring.

## 2. Your Task as a Speaker

As a speaker or as one who arranges for others to speak before older adults, you cannot possibly meet some of the problems mentioned. They come within the jurisdiction of trained social workers, of analysts and psychiatrists, of those who deal with specific phases of gerontology, gerontomy and geriatrics.

Yet, it is well for you to know these problems and thus be in a position to plan your talks in a helpful way, with due regard to the age, environment and frame of mind of your listeners.

You or the speaker selected can give your listeners hope, courage and inspiration. You can regenerate and revitalize their flagging spirits and point out the benefits of older age. You can show them how to widen their horizons, broaden their concepts, find new interests and learn to live with their aches and pains and the growing restrictions normal and natural with advancing years. All of this can be achieved through the proper choice of speech material and the way it is presented.

## 3. What Interests Senior Adults?

The older adult is interested in everything pertaining to man's march through the ages. Yet, in most cases, he is much

more interested in matters about himself, about self-better-
ment and self-improvement, about ways and means to get
more out of life within his restricted capacities and within
the limitations of his age. He wants to know how to deal with
many things and among them are:

1—How to disassociate himself from old routines and
activities which are often only a painful reminder of a life
that used to be.

2—How to acquire new habits and modes of living in
keeping with his advanced age and new status as a man of
leisure.

3—How to banish minor fears, worries or anxieties and
readily adapt himself to the changes within him and the existing attitudes toward him.

4—How to overcome his lingering feeling that he is not
wanted or needed and can still be useful in various ways.

5—How to make time count in his favor and how to live
with himself and others, within his growing limitations.

6—How to make the most of his idle time and how to
participate in suitable educational and recreational activities.

7—How to deal with his inner conflicts and overcome his
loneliness or the feeling of insecurity.

8—How to gain self-confidence, retain his self-respect
and at the same time satisfy his desire for self-expression.

9—How to find companionship and how to make friends
without having to "buy his way in" or be subservient to anyone in any way.

10—How to be helpful to others and put his skills, knowledge, experience and background to better use.

11—How to gain commendation and recognition among
his fellow men and feel that he is part of them.

12—How to attain spiritual belief and, if he wandered off course, how to find his way back to God.

## 4. Guideposts for Speakers

The twelve general areas of interest enumerated will always find an appreciative audience among older adults. Intermix such topics with authoritative talks on health, nutrition, travel, current affairs, popular book reviews, social arts, modern discoveries, legal pointers or popular psychology, and those speeches will surely give your listeners something they want and something they enjoy hearing.

Make sure to use the positive approach and be specific in your explanations. Whenever possible use illustrations or examples familiar to your audience. If you are suggesting certain steps, let them be simple and easy to follow.

A teacher in public speaking suggested to his students to use the "p-o-w-e-r" formula for the preparation of an effective speech. It has considerable merit and could become your guide in planning speeches for senior adults.

The formula is as follows:

P—Prepare your speech with the particular audience in mind and present it as clearly and distinctly as you can.

O—Omit conflicting viewpoints. Avoid trite clichés, worn expressions and banal platitudes.

W—Weave your talk around your basic theme and do not wander off into strange fields or by-paths.

E—Explain and exemplify the important points by using simple examples and familiar comparisons.

R—Repeat the main points in different words and in different ways. Let them add *power* to your speech.

That appears to be sound advice and here are a few more practical tips:

1—Never talk above the heads of your listeners or try to impress them with your knowledge and importance.

2—Never talk too fast, too slow, too long or indulge in histrionics.

3—Never advance unfounded claims, wild surmises or false contentions. Someone in your audience may know more about your subject matter than you and take the notion to put you to shame.

4—Never talk down to your listeners or assume a patronizing attitude.

5—Try to bring your audience into the picture as soon as possible or else identify yourself with your listeners. Be one of them for the time being and they will "love" you for it.

### 5. How to Treat a Senior Adult Audience

Whether your audience is large or small you will find that older persons are quick to detect pretense and insincerity. They dislike condescension. They want to be given due respect for their age, for their knowledge or maturity, and be looked upon as total entities.

With those things in mind here are twelve suggestions on how to treat a senior adult audience:

1—Phrase your thoughts sharply, clearly. Let your words be like a mirror reflecting everything you say as distinctly as possible.

2—Choose simple words. Do not wax too eloquent, too academic or too erudite. Let the words you use serve their basic purpose, to clarify, to amplify, to fortify or to intensify the underlying theme and purpose of your talk.

3—Watch your articulation and enunciations. Do not add, drop or transpose syllables. Do not swallow word endings or telescope one word atop another.

4—Be friendly in your presentation but not effusive. Be warm but not exuberant, courteous but not prissy, dignified but not stuffy or stodgy.

5—Be natural in your delivery. Avoid abrupt changes in your speech melody. Do not shout or whisper unnecessarily and do not imbue ordinary words and phrases with meanings beyond their usual interpretations.

6—Avoid calling attention to your clothes, gestures, mannerisms or general behavior. Your main purpose is to tell, to inform, to educate or inspire your listeners and not to display your idiosyncracies.

7—Adapt your mode of delivery to the immediate need, to the acoustics of the room and the number of people listening to you. Many an older person is not so quick to grasp something entirely new to him.

8—Be cognizant of the fact that older adults are more sensitive to physical discomforts and disturbing elements. Open windows, drafts, too much heat or cold, poor lighting, bad acoustics, a rasping voice, street noises, a rambling delivery, poor seating arrangements, a lengthy diatribe or off-color stories, to mention only a few annoyances, may upset your listeners and quickly nullify a well-prepared and well-presented talk.

9—Keep in mind the possible physical infirmities and sense impairments of your listeners. Some of them may not see or hear so well and most of them cannot remain too long in one position. If your talk is to last more than forty minutes, have a break in between. Give your audience the chance to stand up, to stretch and to leave the room for a few minutes.

10—If your talk deals with something new, tie it in with the old and the familiar. Many an older person is set in his ways of thinking and if what you say is a radical departure from what is usually accepted, go about it in a gradual manner. Do it without being patronizing or dictatorial.

11—Be especially careful not to go off at a tangent or advance wild assertions. Some of your listeners may be well versed in that field and put you in a bad light during the question and answer period.

12—Most audiences, and senior adult listeners are no exception, are quick to judge a speaker not only by what he says but also how he says it. If you know your subject and present it properly they will listen attentively or else lose interest and their restlessness will soon become apparent.

These guideposts will work well not only with older adults but with any audience. They are axiomatic of all effective speeches.

### 6. How to Handle Self-Improvement Topics

If your talks deal with personal development and self-improvement, stress the fact that it is never too late to start, that no matter how far away the goal might be, the mere striving for it is an accomplishment.

Emphasize the opportunities the older person has to follow a given inclination, to do some of the things he always wanted to do but never had the time for it until now.

Dwell upon the fallacy of trying to live in three different worlds at the same time: in the past, in the present and in the future. Urge your listeners to unburden themselves of the mistakes of the past or the unpleasantness of yesterday, to stop fretting about the probabilities of tomorrow and to overlook some of the annoyances of today.

Use specific examples to tell how older persons CAN learn new things, make new friends, develop new interests, cultivate new concepts and find self-expression within the limitations of their age, abilities and surroundings.

Stress to each listener the fact that the future he waited for, saved for, worked for and planned for is here. His battles are won and his main concern at the moment should be how to live better and how to enjoy more fully his immediate present. Emphasize over and over again that although he may not be as spry and alert as in years past and although he is restricted in some of his activities, quite a few of the good things in this great, big, wonderful world of ours are his to have and to enjoy. Impress upon him the many avenues open to him if he would learn to see as well as to look, to listen as well as to hear, with his eyes, his ears and his heart.

## 7. How to Tie in Extraneous Subjects

If your talk deals with food, diet, nutrition, travel, medicine, history, science, habits, behavior, music or the arts, look for ways to bring your listeners into the picture as soon as you can. Pass out maps, samples, folders, resumés or other descriptive material pertaining to your talk.

In the case of a travelogue, mention over and over again the broadening educational values of armchair trips. In the case of educational or scientific topics, stress the ways of how easy it is to learn more about the same topics through books and magazines, available free of charge from the nearest public library.

If your speeches deal with developments and discoveries, bring into your talk specific examples of how and where amateurs often blazed a trail and spearheaded the initial efforts which led to the given discovery or development. Challenge your listeners to try their hand at something similar in such fields with which they are familiar, or where their special skills, knowledge or background might be utilized.

If your talks are meant only to amuse or entertain, stress the value of fun and laughter in their social and personal use. Show how a sense of humor can lighten a boresome task or how a cheerful attitude dispels worry and discouragement. Urge your listeners to read books and magazines of humorous content and of an inspirational character which tend to energize and add to the joys of living.

In other words, form connecting links between your talks and your listeners through the proper uses of contrast and comparison, of inference and association, of analogy and direct suggestions. Let the steps you suggest be like a stairway that will lead your audience to new heights and show them how to add value and meaning to their leisure hours.

## 8. How to Enhance the Value of a Speech

As a speaker before older people, especially if your talks are part of an educational and inspirational program, you can play an important part in building listener interest and participation. You can make your gatherings the highlight of the day or week. You can turn your meetings into an interesting and enjoyable time by utilizing one of more of these ideas:

1—Leave ample time toward the end of your speech for questions and answers. As a matter of fact, it would be well to stress it before you start speaking and give the impression to your listeners that the question and answer period is the most important phase of your talk.

2—Encourage the members of your audience to ask questions. Pay particular attention to those people who appear to be too timid or hesitant. And when they do muster enough courage to get up to speak, compliment them on the aptness, seriousness or timeliness of the question, even when such is not always the case.

3—Be quick to discourage the garrulous extrovert who tries to monopolize the floor or wants to "sound off" just to hear his own voice. Do it in a polite but firm manner.

4—Put a time limit on all questions to be asked and let no one speak more than once on the same topic unless you consider it expedient or interesting to the rest. Explain your stand on the matter, namely, that you want as many different questions from the floor as possible and the more people participating in it the better.

5—Insist that all questions deal with the subject matter. But make allowances for minor deviations, especially for those members of your audience who are neophytes and are diffident or self-conscious.

6—If some of your listeners insist on asking irrelevant questions, pass them off lightly, without showing impatience or displeasure.

7—If the questions do not come readily, assume that you are one of the typical listeners and propose one or more questions of your own. Let them be the obvious kind, questions which the average person is apt to ask. Make believe they are questions asked of you at some other time or place and go on from there.

## 9. How to Get Listener Participation

If your talk deals with travel, science, education or other topics which do not lend themselves to questioning, ask listeners to tell briefly of trips they took, of places they saw; or if some of them came originally from some other country, to tell something of customs and traditions in their old homeland. In other words, draw upon the members of your audience for little talks or for comments and let each person feel important for the moment. Furthermore, be sure to mention them by name and to express your appreciation for their assistance and cooperation.

And, if you expect to give a series of talks before the same group and want to involve them in the talks as part of a prearranged therapeutic project, introduce innovations in some of these ways:

1—Announce that for your next meeting you intend to use native talent, "experts" and "authorities" drawn from the members of your audience. Treat those appelations with a touch of whimsy. Allay the fears that any one of the experts appearing with you will be placed in a poor light. Ask for volunteers to serve on your panel of experts and urge the hesitant ones to get up and be counted.

2—Try to get a fair representation of both sexes to serve as members of your panel and limit the number to four or five. Tell them what the topic will be and urge each participant to gather necessary data. You will be giving the panelists something to do and enable them to be in the limelight for a while. And what wonderful mental therapy it is!

3—Be sure to get some background for each panelist who appears on the program, and while he or she takes the proper place near you, give him the proper "send off." Let each expert have his moment of glory while he holds the center of the stage. Make each presentation sound good, even if all you can say is that the person in question is an ardent worker, was a good parent, is a loyal friend, was good in his chosen work or is friendly, dependable, cooperative, etc.

4—Act as the moderator or pace setter and start the forum, symposium or panel discussion only with brief introductory remarks. Let the panelists carry the ball and speak for the time allotted. Tie in their separate talks with a simple summary, and ask the listeners to address their questions to each panelist by his name or by the number on the panel.

5—If any one of your expectant panelists is somewhat hesitant about his participation, have a private talk with him, help him make an outline or coach him a little. If all of your panelists are fearful, have a couple of rehearsals with them privately and without the knowledge of the rest of the group.

6—If your attempt to have a panel does not meet with ready approval, try again a little while later, or have fewer members on the panel, or select a different topic, or have private talks with likely panelists before you make a public request.

7—Be sure to retain a firm hold on the proceedings after the panel and the subject matter are selected. Do not let the talks degenerate into desultory remarks and leave no room for spiteful comments or personal gibes. In other words, let your listeners disagree as much as they wish with what a given panelist said but not with the panelist himself.

## 10. How to Secure Suitable Speakers

If you had little experience in contacting or engaging speakers and lecturers, you would do well to consult your local senior citizen's center, the committee on aging, the community centers or the social service agencies in your city, especially if you are not in a position to pay for the speaker's time.

Speakers and lecturers can be drawn from a number of sources at no cost to your group. Among them are:

1—Your city or county sponsored lecturer's forum, which can provide speakers and lecturers for series of talks, providing certain simple requirements are met by your group.

2—Your adult education center, sponsored by your board of education and arranged through your nearest adult school principal.

3—Your county medical association, working through your local hospitals and welfare agencies, will often supply you with medical men to speak on mental hygiene and health problems.

4—Your local cancer, TB association, heart foundation and similar agencies will be glad to supply you with speakers to touch upon the symptoms, dangers and treatment of ailments in their respective fields.

5—Your nearest college or university can be called upon for graduates or instructors to speak on many subjects.

6—Your Toastmaster clubs as well as the various service organizations such as the Kiwanis, Rotary, Lions and Soroptomists can often supply you with speakers from their ranks. Or they may be willing to underwrite speakers to meet your needs.

7—The church federations in the various denominations are often in a position to supply you with speakers, and in some instances they will sponsor certain speakers for you.

8—The fraternal lodges, sisterhoods and community centers often have access to or can supply you from time to time with suitable speakers.

9—The members of your local gerontological society, as well as clinical and analytical psychologists who work through various welfare agencies, are a good source of speaker material.

10—The "Forty Plus" club, the labor unions, the bar association and various groups from your local chamber of commerce will usually be glad to supply you with speakers.

11—Your local police, fire and health departments, as well as various governmental agencies that deal with specific needs and problems in your community, can often be called upon to supply speakers.

12—The local Social Security office, the Income Revenue department, the Postal Inspection office, as well as various civic and welfare groups in your city, will often provide speakers to cover details and operations within their specified fields.

There are other groups, such as trade associations, travel agencies, schools for the blind and the mentally retarded, dieticians, music teachers, oil companies, business firms, art galleries, local libraries, consulates of foreign offices, stamp collectors, to mention but a few of them, that can be called upon from time to time. They will often supply you with films as well as speakers at no cost to your group.

On the other hand, there may be qualified men and women within your own group who could easily undertake to give a series of talks on matters pertaining to their own knowledge and experience. There may be doctors, lawyers, teachers, engineers, designers, die makers, travelers, biologists, business executives, and a host of others who could give interesting talks.

It may be a matter of only discussing it in private and working out a suitable series of talks. It may require only some preparation in gathering the necessary material and in that your nearest librarian could be of great help to you.

Check into these various avenues for speaker material, and before long you will be able to arrange the kind of speeches that your group will welcome every time.

# CHAPTER EIGHTEEN

# How to Start a Senior Adult Group

Are you looking for things to do that are creative and will bring you a sense of accomplishment? Are there any projects or activities you would like to undertake with others close to your age and unite efforts for all concerned? Are such groups active in your community? Have you attended any of their meetings? Do they have anything to offer you?

If not, why not form a senior group of your own? It is not so difficult and it does not require special talents, prerequisites or extra expenditures. Even if you lack the executive ability and have had no organizational experience you can try your hand at it because in many cases you will be able to get the help needed from those who have the professional "know-how."

In most cases the formation of a senior adult group is mainly a matter of talking to and bringing people together. The procedure is simple. You begin with the people you know and you ask them to suggest the names of other prospective members. You can start with your pastor or preacher, with your rabbi or your priest. Discuss it with the officers of your local civic, service, business and fraternal groups. Speak with your public officials, with the alderman or councilman of your district, with the representative of your union, trade or business organization. Then ask your city editor of the local paper to give your idea a little publicity.

You will find that nearly everyone you approach will be interested in your project. The service clubs, such as the Kiwanis, Rotary, Lions, Exchange, Optimists and Soroptomists; the churches, community centers, civic bodies, labor groups and the chamber of commerce; the park and the recreation departments as well as the social service agencies of your city and county and the existing senior adult clubs in cities nearby will be glad to help you form a new group.

As soon as you have the names of twenty or more people, arrange to have a meeting at your home or at some other place and bring up the matter of forming a group in an informal way. Ask for comments and suggestions but retain a firm control over the proceedings. Have 3 x 5 cards ready and let those who are interested become the charter members of the new group. If it is expedient, make provisions then and there for an organizational meeting within the next few days. If not, make a mental note of those whom you feel could meet the need, who expressed a desire to work with you, and let them become the steering or the executive committee.

The details as to when and where to meet, who shall be the officers, what name to adopt, what the membership requirements shall be, what programs to sponsor, what objectives to have and how to finance your projected activities can be taken up later.

If you would prefer to remain on the sidelines for the time being and have someone else handle the formative period details, you may be able to find such a person among the prospective members. He may be a former teacher, social worker, businessman, public official or administrator who would be willing to lend his knowledge and experience to your cause.

Your spiritual leader, an official in public office or the president of one of the service clubs may be willing to assume the responsibility. Or perhaps several of those who attend the initial get-together may wish to work as a committee and thus provide the nucleus of your new group.

On the other hand, it might be an excellent idea for you to be the organizer, if not the leader, even though you may not be sure of yourself and may be somewhat trepidacious about the tasks ahead. For all you know, you may uncover the necessary qualifications within yourself.

Now then, what are the basic qualifications to be a leader or an organizer? Generally speaking, they differ little from those needed to take charge of any group or from instigating and carrying through any undertaking where a number of people work together. What is more, unlike a business venture, it does not require a capital investment in buildings, in machinery or in merchandise. It does not call for personnel management, for detailed plans of operation, for specific knowledge of manufacture or for seasoned experience in marketing and merchandising methods.

To be a leader of a group you need certain attributes but they can be cultivated and acquired as you go along, providing you use common sense and learn to be patient, tolerant, friendly, helpful, cooperative and sincere.

There are two main differences in working with senior adults as compared to people in other age groups:

1—Some of them have held important executive positions in commerce or industry, in teaching or in the professions, in

the scientific world or in an administrative capacity. They may
have a far better background of knowledge and experience
than you and be quick to resent your assumption of authority.
This does not mean that you have to kotow to them or be
subservient in any way.

2—Many older people are set in their ways. They do not
take kindly, quickly or easily, to drastic changes in customary
routines, in their ways of thinking or in their usual modes of
behavior. They dislike the effort to force them into quick
decisions or to be placed in a poor light because of their age
or limitations. They need time to think their way through
before accepting changes or innovations.

As the leader of a senior adult group, you will have to
play many parts. You will have to be the "patient prompter"
to the timid, self-effacing member and the "firm hand" to
the aggressive extrovertive person. You may become the focal
point of jealousy and rivalry, the object of affection or hostility. Yet, you will have to refrain at all times from becoming
emotionally involved with any particular member of your
group.

As the leader you will be expected to remain helpful, considerate and sympathetic at all times. Members will look to
you for program ideas and suggestions yet at the same time
will want to be free to approve or disapprove. The objections
may stem from sensitivity about their growing infirmities or
from concern about possible tiring involvments. In some instances, special coaching may be required before the members will be ready to accept a given plan or take part in a
proposed undertaking.

As the leader of a senior adult group you may often have
to be the arbitrator as well as the arbiter in settling disputes
between members and remain fair and impartial in the face

of strong feeling and personal preference. It will be up to you to make allowances for differences in views and opinions, as such are affected by feelings or preferences, by background or by past experience. And your actions and behavior will become the example to be followed by the rest.

As the leader it will be up to you to maintain a congenial atmosphere at all meetings, to prevent the formation of disruptive cliques, to encourage wholehearted participation in the various activities and to develop leadership among those who have the potentialities and can assume given responsibilities.

As the leader it will be up to you to engender a feeling of friendship and cooperation. It will be part of your task to inculcate the sense of belonging and being an important part of the group. This is most essential, especially to many an older person who feels insecure in his status, who is quick to be offended or believes that he is being slighted, who wants to feel that he is important and wanted by somebody and who seeks recognition and commendation.

One of the ways to achieve this desirable relationship between members is to make each one of them feel important. Let each member feel that he has a voice in all proceedings, that every program and activity is planned for his benefit and sense of well-being. Encourage open discussions. Let each idea be aired at open meetings and nothing be undertaken without the sanction of all, unless a committee has been chosen and is empowered to handle all the details of a proposed activity.

You might ask, have I the qualifications needed to assume the leadership of a group? If you have your doubts, ask these questions of yourself:

1—Are you motivated by a genuine interest in other senior adults and are you sincere in your desire to work with them?

2—Are you emotionally attuned to associate more often with other senior adults and accept them as they are?

3—Are you willing to share with others the things you know and can do well, without any reservations?

4—Can you remain fair and impartial when called upon to settle a dispute where your close friends are involved?

5—Can you inspire loyalty and take opposition and criticism as they come?

6—Can you keep from favoring one person and ignoring another for selfish or personal reasons?

7—Can you delegate duties by picking the most likely person for each job and thus develop leadership?

8—Do you know how to encourage the timid and build up their self-confidence?

9—Can you redirect the activities of the overaggressive extrovert into desirable and constructive channels?

10—Can you instigate and carry through given plans against the opposition of those who have axes to grind and marshal the strength of others behind you?

11—Are you big enough to say "I'm sorry" when need be, and step back so that someone else will have the limelight for a while?

12—Can you make a quick change when necessary and adapt yourself quickly to a new need or situation?

If your answer to these questions is an unqualified "YES!" you are leader material, and whatever be the size of the new group you are starting you will be a successful leader.

There are proven ways to retain member interest and assure better attendance at meetings. Among them are:

1—The selection of a proper, convenient meeting place and the careful planning of activities. Your meeting place should have adequate lighting facilities, good heating and ventilation, comfortable seating, proper lounging and kitchen facilities, a minimum of stairs to climb, be centrally located and easily accessible by public transportation. This may seem to be a difficult thing to do, but, surprisingly enough, many churches, civic groups, fraternal orders, service organizations and community centers often have such accommodations and in many instances they can be obtained by groups such as yours at a moderate rental.

2—The business end of your general meetings should be held down to a minimum. Let all the planning, the preparing and handling of various proposed activities be entrusted to committees. It is a good idea to plan programs two and three months in advance. It is also desirable to undertake at least one long-time project of a civic or communal nature.

3—The programs should embrace activities on a social, cultural and educational level, and be so diversified that every member could participate and become identified with one or more of the activities.

Under the social heading would come table games, dancing, picnics, musicales, birthday parties and excursions. Under the educational and cultural heading you could have lectures, reviews, discussions, open forums, travelogues, arts and crafts and day classes. Under the recreational and group participation heading would be folk dancing, nature walks, community singing, sewing or knitting bees, bridge tournaments, amateur productions, various workshops, public speaking and music appreciation classes.

Many classes can be arranged through your local adult schools. In many instances, a group of twenty-five or more adults who make a written request to their Adult School Department or to their local board of education can have a teacher or lecturer assigned to them for daytime or evening meetings at no cost to the group.

4—Have numerous permanent and special committees and let each member be the head of or part of a given committee. Among the permanent committees are membership, entertainment, hospitality, social, publicity, educational, refreshments, scholarships, grievance and ways and means. Among the special committees are all those of a temporary nature and will include special affairs undertaken only from time to time.

Each committee can be subdivided and have its specific responsibilities. For instance, the membership can have a subcommittee devoting itself to secure new members, another to keep track of members who do not come regularly to meetings, another to arrange transportation for those who find it difficult to come via public conveyances and still another subcommittee to provide "big brothers" or "big sisters" for members who need physical and moral support.

In addition, special posts can be created to make given members feel that they are needed, wanted and add something to the welfare of the group. Among such posts can be, chairman of the day, buyer of gifts for birthdays and anniversaries, keeper of song books and music records, custodian of supplies, monitor on walks and excursions, recorder of special events, photographer, official greeter and keeper of attendance records. Some members may like the idea of conducting small classes of their own and teach others the things they know well. There also may be members who would visit other similar groups and serve as roving reporters.

These are just a few of the ways to use to keep things moving. To supplement these ideas be sure to utilize the "resource" material available. You will find it in books, pamphlets, brochures, committee reports and in a number of periodicals devoted to the interests of senior adults. Some of this material can be had through your local library and from the files of various community agencies in your city.

Among the church denominations which have specific material and sponsor senior adult groups among their members, the following is only a partial list:

The National Council of the Churches of Christ, 257 Fourth Ave., New York 10, N. Y.; American Baptist Churches, 1703 Chestnut St., Philadelphia; Indiana Council of Churches, 2342 East 66th St., Indianapolis; National Catholic Welfare Conference, 1312 Massachusetts Ave., N.W. Washington 5, D. C.; Congressional Christian Churches, 14 Beacon St., Boston, and 19 La Salle St., Chicago; Evangelical and Reformed Churches, 1505 Race St., Philadelphia; The Methodist Church, P. O. Box 871, Nashville, Tenn.; The Presbyterian Churches, P. O. Box 1176, Richmond, Va.; The Montana Methodist Conference, 126 Fourth Ave., Kalispel, Mont.; The United Churches of Canada, 209 Queen St. West, Toronto, Ontario, Canada.

Send a letter to the Department of Adult Work or to the Department of Education at any of these churches and you will have a prompt reply. Or, if you would rather have someone else do it for you, consult your pastor, preacher, rabbi or reverend and he will be glad to help you. He will get the "resource" material available and lend a willing hand to the formation of a senior adult group in your community.

As to the various agencies sponsored by the city, county or state, and the various organizations that are composed of or work with senior adults, the partial list given below can serve as your guide to similar agencies and organizations within your own community.

California Coordinating Committee on Aging, 1025 P St., Sacramento 2, Calif.; California Institute of Social Welfare, 1031 So. Grand Ave., Los Angeles 15, Calif.; Los Angeles County Senior Citizens Service Center, 306 West Third St., Los Angeles 54, Calif.; United Senior Citizens of San Gabriel Valley, 380 Rosemont Ave., Pasadena 3, Calif.; National League of Senior Citizens, 1031 So. Grand Ave., Los Angeles 15, Calif.; Senior Citizens Association of Los Angeles County, 1547 Corinth Ave., West Los Angeles, Calif.; Florida Council for the Aging, St. Petersburg, Fla.; National Committee on Aging, 1790 Broadway, New York 19, N. Y.; New York State Association of Social Agencies, 105 East 22nd St., New York 10, N. Y.; American Society for the Aged, 590 Fifth Ave., New York 36, N. Y.; New York State Committee on the Problems of the Aged, 94 Broadway, Newburgh, N. Y.

Chicago Welfare Council, 135 W. Madison St., Chicago 2, Ill.; Allegheny County Health and Welfare Federation, 200 Rose St., Pittsburgh 19, Pa.; Community Welfare Council, 14 West Jackson St., Madison, Wis.; Cleveland Welfare Federation, 1000 Hudson St., Cleveland 15, Ohio; Philadelphia Recreation Association, 1427 Spruce St., Philadelphia 2, Pa.; University of Chicago, Gerontology Division, Ann Arbor, Mich.; XYZ (X-tra Years of Zest) Club, First Methodist Church, Montgomery, Ala.; Arizona Senior Citizens Committee, 827 East Second St., Tucson, Ariz.

Colorado League of Senior Citizens, 1536 So. Akoma St., Denver, Colo.; St. Petersburg Hospitality Center, 137 Central Ave., St. Petersburg, Fla.; Louisiana League of Senior Citizens, 1216 Center St., New Iberia, La.; Happy Hours Club, Jefferson Ave. Baptist Church, Detroit, Mich.; Hennepin County Welfare Board, 134 Court St., Minneapolis, Minn.; Social Security Senior Citizens, 61 Van Hooten St., Patterson, N. J.; National Federation of Old Age, 710 Jefferson St., Spokane, Wash.

In publications devoted to the interests of senior adults, to mention some of them, are: The Journal of Gerontology, published by the Gerontological Society of America and available at your local public library; The Senior Citizen Sentinel, 1031 So. Grand Ave., Los Angeles 15, Calif.; The Modern Maturity Magazine, American Association of Retired Person, 310 East Grand Ave., Ojai, Calif.; Mature Years Magazine, Graded Press, 810 Broadway, Nashville 2, Tenn.; Journal of Lifetime Living, 1625 Bay Rd., Miami Beach, Fla.; Senior Citizens Magazine, 1129 Vermont Ave. N.W., Washington 5, D. C.; Aging, a government publication, subscribed through the Superintendent of Documents, Government Printing Office, Washington, D. C.; Adult Leadership Magazine, Adult Education Association, 743 No. Wabash Ave., Chicago, Ill.; Harvest Years, 681 Market St., San Francisco 5, Calif.

Check with the groups closest to you. Get copies of the magazines mentioned and ask the editors for suggestions and material they might have on the formation of senior adult groups. Most everyone will be glad to help you and you will find ready support from public officials, civic bodies, trade unions, service organizations and spiritual leaders in your community.

There is no greater inner joy and personal satisfaction than to help your fellow men and to foster the spirit of good fellowship and brotherhood among all people. Do some of these things, even on a small scale, and no matter what your age, sex, looks, abilities or circumstances, people will "look up" to you and gladly follow your lead. Do some of these things and you will add new values and meanings to your day-by-day living as you truly find the gold in your golden age.

May God be with you on this day and all the days yet to come.